D1360473

Shopping List for Murder

The TRUE STORY of a 1960s victim of horrific sexual abuse and mind control, who was driven to a desperate act, and the courageous lawyer who set her free

Tess McCormack

TO GIL

For all you have done for me

Gil turned and addressed the jurors: "At this time, sir, I wish to advise the jury about the notes that were written by the defendant, Katherine Kunz. She does not deny, nor has she ever denied writing them. Her only denial is in the interpretation of them. They are just the fantasy of a woman under a lot of stress."

Branti jumped to his feet, the veins in his neck visible**: "Fantasy, hell!" he bellowed. "It's a shopping list for murder!"**

PROLOGUE

1973

A red cape and a matching red beret worn at a tilt laid a dubious claim to smartness and did little to conceal her pregnancy. Her tumescent belly contrasted with the thinness of her pale, tear-stained face; the short brown hair stuck out in unkempt clumps.

The chair groaned loudly as Gil McCormack, Esq., leaned back, flipping his pencil and catching it in precise, measured motions. Opposing counsel often complained it was a ploy deliberately used to mesmerize the jurors and distract them from concentrating on testimony. Gil insisted it was unconscious and helped him think.

Either this young woman was deranged, or she had an extraordinarily rich fantasy life. Observing her nervous tugs at her fingers, he offered her a cigarette, but she declined.

"Mrs. Kunz, how tall are you, and how much do you weigh?"

"I'm five two, and my normal weight is about one hundred fourteen."

"And your mother?"

"She's about four-eleven and weighs maybe a hundred and five pounds."

"How big is the other girl?"

"She's a little taller than I am but heavier—I couldn't pick her up."

"I see you have bruises on your arm. How did that happen?"

"She bit me! When I tried to pull her off my mother, she bit me, so, when I saw the frying pan on the stove, I picked it up and hit her with it. The next thing I remember, the police were there."

* * *

His wife, Tess, came to work for McCormack some sixteen years earlier. She still worked for him, had indeed become his office manager.

Later that night, as they were having dinner, he asked, "Did you happen to see Mrs. Kunz in the office today?"

"The pregnant Little Red Riding Hood?"

Tess's sharp observations always made McCormack smile. "Yes. She told me a story so bizarre I had a hard time believing it. I even made her tell it twice, and I don't think she was lying. There is something about her— I feel bad for her, anyway."

"What's she being charged with?"

"Attempted murder."

CHAPTER 1

1936–1939

As most of the folks around 14th Street in Brooklyn knew, the corset lady was an unrepentant gossip. Pulling the strings tightly around Marion Mulrooney's waist, she asked, "D'ya know Mrs. Edwards? That nice pregnant Italian lady around the corner, with the little kid, Freddie?"

Marion didn't, but was always open to hearing a juicy story. "What about her?"

"Ya won't believe it when I tell ya. It happened right before my eyes. I still get the shivers when I think of it."

"Fer Chrissake, will ya tell me already?"

"Well, I'm delivering this here girdle to her, so she should have it for after the baby, ya know? All of a sudden, her face gets beet-red. She jumps up, puts her head in the sink, and runs cold water on her face. She sez, 'I don't feel too good.' So, I say, 'Go lay down, maybe you're on yer feet too much. After all, the baby is due any day, ya know.' Suddenly, she grabs her belly, lets out a helluva scream and falls to the goddamn floor, right in front of my face. *Oy vey!* I jump up and run to her. I slap her face and say, 'Hey, c'mon, no fooling around.' I take one good look at her and I know she ain't fooling around. I get scared shitless, so I run down the hall screaming for help, but it's too late. She's deader than a doorknob! Can you believe it? Right in front of my goddamn eyes, she drops dead! Anyway, Ed—her husband, ya know—is a helluva nice guy, even if he is a cheap bastard. He works on the docks and makes a good buck. If he didn't have any money, I wouldn't care. But I know the guy's loaded! So why the hell should I get stuck with the goddamn girdle? Anyway, what I'm getting at is, he's looking for someone to take care of his kid."

Marion's interest was piqued.

When the corset lady left, Marion called her daughter. In her early twenties, petite and pretty, Alice worked as a live-in domestic in Rutherford, New Jersey, entrusting Marion with the care of her toddler.

"What's the matter, Ma, is Vicki sick?"

"Vicki's fine. I jes' called to let ya know about a terrific job. It's babysitting for some guy whose wife jes' keeled over and died. I hear the guy's loaded! That's why I'm tellin' ya. Ya better not waste any time git'n there."

Alice was pleased to find Ed Edwards gregarious and easygoing. He introduced her to his son, Freddie, a freckle-faced redhead, and invited her to join him for a drink. By the end of the day, she had happily accepted the job.

* * *

One evening, Ed came home early from work and poured himself a whiskey, pensively stirring the ice with his finger. Alice knew something was on his mind but continued washing the dishes, in a hurry to get to her bingo game.

He came up behind her and put his arms around her waist, squeezing her tightly. "Alice . . . whatcha say we git married?"

She looked at him sideways from beneath her eyelashes, her hands submerged in the soapy water. She wanted to say, *What took you so long*, but instead replied sassily, "What? And spoil a good relationship?"

"Ah . . . c'mon Alice, ya know I love ya."

"I'll have to think about it, Ed."

"Think about what?"

"Well, it's…"

"It's what? We git along pretty well, don't we? Anyway, my kid needs a mother, yer kid needs a father, so it makes sense to me." He beamed as he tilted his glass to her. "So whatcha say Alice, huh? Ya wanna git married?"

"I'll letcha know tomorrow."

He swatted her backside.

"Tomorrow, huh? I'll give you five minutes, or I'll change my mind." His laugh was hearty. "In the meantime, I'll fix ya a drink, so we can celebrate."

Alice dried her hands on her apron, threw it on the kitchen counter, and followed him into the living room. *What the hell,* she thought, *why not?*

They were married the following weekend.

7

Ed and Alice set up housekeeping in Brooklyn. Her daughter, Vicki, stayed permanently with Marion. Things went well for a while. Children came rapidly—three during just the first three years.

* * *

It was before six in the morning when Alice was awakened by the cry of a hungry child. Slowly, she rolled out of bed and made her way into the kitchen. She took a bottle of milk from the icebox and warmed it under running hot water. As the baby greedily consumed the milk, Alice began the endless chore of collecting dirty clothes. As she sorted the clothes, she emptied pockets, accumulating an interesting assortment of items, including bubble-gum wrappers, toys, and an occasional handkerchief. As she dug into the pockets of Ed's work pants, she discovered a balled-up pay stub. She studied it for a moment, a frown creasing her brow. The name on the pay stub was *Edward Jackson*. She'd never heard of anyone by that name, although she thought she knew most of Ed's friends. What the hell was Ed doing with this guy's pay stub? She shrugged, shoved it into her apron pocket, and continued with the laundry.

When Ed came home that evening, he seemed upset, and quickly went into the kitchen to fix his usual drink. "There's a rumor goin' round that we might be gittin' laid off. I don't think it will affect me, with my seniority an' all, but ya never know. Some of the guys are really upset."

"Speaking of the guys," Alice said, "who the hell is Edward Jackson?"

Ed whipped his head around so fast, his neck twisted like a corkscrew. He was obviously caught off-guard by her question. "Ah, I—I don't know nobody by that name. Why d'ya ask?"

"When I wuz doing the laundry this mornin', I found a pay stub in yer pocket wit that guy's name on it."

"Oh shit," Ed said, sounding relieved, "that's jes' sometin' I found on the docks. I jes' put it in my pocket and forgot about it."

Alice persisted. "If ya don't know the guy why d'ya keep the stub?"

"Git off my back, will ya? I told ya I don't know the guy. Ain't that enough?"

"No, it ain't. It sounds fishy to me. Why the hell can't ya tell me the truth? Does he owe ya some money or sometin'? Are you holding out on me, is that it?"

"Jesus Christ, how many times do I have to tell ya, I don't know the son of a bitch," Ed bellowed, as he opened the door to the closet. "I've had enough of this crap. I'm gonna go down to the bar and have a drink in peace." He reached in, grabbed his hat and coat, and stormed out of the apartment. "And don't bother to wait up for me," he shouted, rumbling down the stairs. "I jes' might not come home tonight."

"Ya bum!" Alice yelled down the hallway after him. "Ya wuz jes' looking for an excuse to go down to the bar. All ya ever want to do anymore is drink, drink, drink!" She slammed the door and slid to the floor, tears streaming down her cheeks.

* * *

Company in the Edwards household was a rarity and a visit from Ed's brother Tom a welcome occurrence. Alice knew little of her husband's family, but what she knew of Tom, soft-spoken and shy, she liked.

She hadn't mentioned the pay stub incident to Ed since the day they fought over it. She hadn't forgotten about it, either.

The opportunity to get some answers came when Ed went into the kitchen to fix the drinks.

"Tom," Alice began, "do ya know anyone by the name of Edward Jackson?"

The smile disappeared from Tom's face. He turned and stared at his sister-in-law.

Alice persisted. "Well? Do ya?"

A nervous cough escaped from Tom's throat as he shifted his weight from one foot to the other.

"I, I...er..." At that moment, Ed appeared with a tray full of drinks.

"Here they are!" he said, putting down the tray. "It's really good to see ya, Tom. Been a coon's age." The brothers lifted their glasses and toasted each other. Ed noticed that Alice wasn't joining them. "Whazza matter, Alice, yer not drinking?"

"No, Ed, I'm not!" She was angry. "Not 'til youse guys tell me what the hell yer hiding from me. I jes' asked yer brother who Edward Jackson is, and he looked like he saw a ghost." She turned to her brother-in-law and snapped, "I thought ya wuz my friend, Tom, but I can see ya know *sometin'* ya ain't tellin me."

Tom cast a nervous glance at his brother. Ed took a deep gulp from his glass and remained silent.

"Well, Alice," Tom replied uneasily, "I don't know what he calls himself, but my name is Thomas Jackson."

Alice's mouth hung open. She looked at her husband in bewilderment. In an almost inaudible whisper, she asked, "Why the hell did ya lie to me?" Her voice rapidly rose to a screech. "Ya lying son of a bitch! What the hell ya got to hide?"

Ed glanced at his brother, then at his distraught wife. "Well," he said, putting a comforting arm around Alice's shoulders, "let's have another drink and I'll tell ya the whole story. It's really nothin' to get excited about. It's really very simple."

Two bottles later, Ed was still explaining. His words by then were slurred, his eyes watery. "Ya see, Alice, it's like this . . . Freddie's mother and me wuz never married. We jes' lived together, see? The reason wuz, she wuz already married; her husband wuz in the can, Mafia, ya know? When she got pregnant, we moved to Jersey 'cause we didn't want nobody to know where we wuz. She wuz afraid that if her old man found out she wuz knocked up, he'd probably send some hood to kill her . . . and probably me, too. So, we decided to change our name so nobody could find us."

He took a handkerchief from his pocket and wiped his face. "Then I get this call one day at work, and some lady's screaming, 'Yer wife is *dead*!' What the hell could I do? I still had a kid to take care of. And anyway, what the hell difference does it make? Everybody at work knew me as Ed Edwards, so I never changed it. Then ya came along and . . . hell, ya know the rest."

Alice listened, realizing how little she really knew about him.

10

He turned to his brother for support. "What could I do, Tom? I did the best I could."

Ed turned to his silent wife, reached for her hand, and looked into her eyes. "I couldn't of made it without you, Alice, honest. Ya know I love ya, dontcha? It's like I said, everybody already knew me by that name, so I said, 'What the hell difference does it make?' It's only a name."

Alice shook her head, her voice shrill. "What *difference* does it make? Are you kiddin'? We got kids whose names we gotta change, that's all, you stupid mick!"

Ed grinned, grabbed her around the waist, and lifted her into the air. "I'll tell ya what, Alice, we'll change the kids' names, and then we'll git married again!" He turned to his brother. "And this time, Tom here can be our best man." Ed squeezed his brother in a bear hug. "Whaddaya say, Tom, huh? Ya wanna be our best man?"

"It's okay with me, but I think you'd better talk to your wife and get this mess straightened out. Maybe I ought to go home and let you two talk."

"Nah, don't go, Tom. We ain't got nothin' to talk about, right, Alice?"

Alice was silent.

"See? I told ya she ain't mad no more. I told ya it was no big deal. Whaddaya say we have another drink to celebrate? Me and my ole lady are gonna git married." Ed turned to his wife, lifting his glass in a toast, and said, "I promise!"

The names of the children were changed and a wedding date set. However, Alice soon discovered she was pregnant again. She decided to wait until after the baby was born before she set a new date.

About a month after the birth of Anna, Alice and Ed were getting ready for bed when the doorbell rang. "Who the hell can that be at this hour?" asked Ed.

"What the hell ya asking me fer? It sure as hell ain't fer me. It's probably one of your cronies looking fer a free drink."

Ed picked up his pants from where he'd tossed them on the side chair and headed, barefooted, through the living room to the door. Alice got into bed, but the sounds of angry voices reached her. At first, the voices appeared loud, then—quite strangely, she thought—fell to a

11

whisper. As tired as she was, she got out of bed, put on her robe, and entered the living room. Ed was standing in the doorway, holding the door ajar. She could see a slightly built woman in her early thirties, standing behind a tall, burly man, who was speaking with Ed.

"You might as well come in," Ed said, resigned. "It don't make no difference now. Wanna drink? I think we're all gonna need one by the time this is over."

Alice's face was a mask of bewilderment. "Ed, who are these people? Ain't ya gonna introduce me?"

"Sure," he said. "Alice—" he bent forward in an exaggerated bow, "meet my wife. Her name is also Alice. She just served me with divorce papers!"

"Divorce papers? Oh, my God. Ya mean yer *already married?*" With both hands on her hips, Alice screamed at a high pitch, "No wonder ya couldn't stay sober long enough to marry me. Ya no-good son of a bitch!"

Ed turned to the uninvited guests. "Goddamn it, if yer coming in, come in! If yer not, get the hell out! We don't have to put on a show for the whole goddamn building, do we?"

Alice buried her head in her hands and broke into sobs. "I can't believe it! I've got six kids and now I find out he's married. *Ya bastard! Ya no-good son of a bitch!* What the hell am I gonna do now?"

* * *

1959

Alice sat on the edge of the bed, her body scarcely denting it. She looked into the mirror that hung on the back of her bedroom door. She fingered her hair, now thin and gray, and remembered the day after Ed's funeral, when in anger, she had chopped it all off. "The merry widow," her friends had called her, but to her, destroying the very thing Ed had loved about her most—her long, shiny black hair—was an act of unburdening herself.

Although Ed had promised to marry her when his divorce became final, he couldn't stay sober long enough to go through with it. He lost his job; things went sour. Alice attempted to get a hysterectomy, but the doctor refused her request because her 'husband' withheld consent. With nowhere to go and no other means of support, she continued to live with Ed and bore him four more children. It all seemed so long ago. *Damn that Ed! The best thing he ever did fer me was die . . . and he didn't do that soon enough*

CHAPTER 2

1959

It had been Bobby who brought Peter home. At first, Alice was pleased. He seemed like such a nice boy, though he had not yet become completely Americanized and still spoke with a German accent. Whenever Bobby saw Peter coming, he would make his brothers and sisters line up, stand at attention, and give the 'Heil, Hitler!' salute. When Alice heard the chanting, she would run out, sometimes swinging a wooden spoon, to make them stop.

But her defense of Peter ended when she discovered that he was the reason her daughter Kathy had started playing hooky from school. Of all her children, she was the quiet one, the bookworm who wanted to be a nurse.

One morning, when Alice came home from work at four a.m., she discovered that Kathy was still out.

Reaching for the kettle and filling it with water, Alice put it on the stove, then sat down heavily at the kitchen table and lit a cigarette. Her back and shoulders ached from scrubbing the long hallways of the building where she worked for a little extra cash to supplement her welfare benefits.

She dozed for a few minutes, forcing herself up when she heard the whistle of the boiling kettle. She would have to deal with Kathy's behavior. After drinking her tea slowly, she lit another cigarette and then finished it. Kathy still hadn't come in. Finally, resting her arms on the kitchen table, Alice put her head down and fell asleep.

She jumped when she heard the sound of a key turning in the lock. By the time the door opened, Alice was wide awake.   "Where the hell have ya been?" she screamed. "Do you know what time it is?"

The cat, who had been asleep on the kitchen table, jumped to the floor and scampered to safety.

Kathy slumped in the doorway, shoes dangling from her fingertips, her mouth open but mute, her face flushed. Her clothes were wrinkled, she reeked of perfume, but her hair had recently been combed and fell in

14

beguiling curls around her face. She stared at her mother, making no attempt to reply, shifting her weight from one bare foot to the other.

"Answer me!" Alice shouted. "Where the hell have ya been?"

"With Peter."

"Well," Alice said, planting her hands firmly on her hips, "I assumed that much. But where? And what were ya doin', playin' tiddlywinks?"

The more Alice yelled, the angrier she became. "I can't go to work and worry all night where the hell ya are! Tomorrow I'm callin' Peter's father! This shit's gotta stop. I'm gonna tell him to keep Peter away from this house, 'cause yer not gonna be allowed to see him no more!"

Kathy's eyes opened wide. "No, Momma, please don't say that! I'll die if I can't see Peter anymore. I *love* him, Momma, *please.*"

"Love? What the hell d'ya know 'bout love? Yer still wet behind the ears. Now, git the hell to bed before I give ya a good kick in the ass. If yer old man wuz here ya wouldn't be able to sit fer a week. And another thing, don't let me hear ya played hooky no more, either, or yer really goin' get it!"

"I don't want to go to school anymore, Momma."

"What the hell ya talkin' about? "

"I changed my mind, Momma. I just want to be with Peter."

"Jesus Christ! Before ya met that jerk, all ya ever talked about wuz bein' a nurse. Now all of a sudden, ya don't wanna do nothin'. I always said ya wuz jes' like yer ole man, smart but stupid and yer goin' do jes' what yer father did—screw everythin' up!"

"Momma, please..." Kathy began but, unable to control her tears, ran from the room.

Alice followed her, but Kathy had thrown herself on her bed, wracked with sobs, blocking any further conversation. Reluctant to awaken the rest of the kids, Alice backed off and returned to the kitchen. With trembling hands, she lit another cigarette. Kids, she thought, goddamn kids.

Alice went through the next twenty-four hours putting food on the table at the usual hours, going off to work again, catnapping when she could. But the following morning, although she hadn't called Peter's father, he appeared at her door.

Oskar Kunz stood in front of her, irritated, impatient. Kathy had phoned Peter to tell him of her mother's threat, and his father had picked up an extension phone and listened.

Alice stared surprised to see him. His dark, piercing eyes glared at her from beneath bushy eyebrows. His short legs looked dwarfed by his barrel-chested body. There was something foreign and commanding about him. She had never liked him, but surely, he would back up her demand that Kathy continue with her education.

She soon discovered how wrong she was. "An education for a woman is a waste of money," he declared with a heavy German accent. "All she needs to know is how to take care of her husband and his needs. I have no objection to my son marrying Katherine. Nature does not call fifteen too young to marry. In Europe, we know better."

Alice's voice rose. "This is *America.* I don't give a goddamn what they do in Europe. I'm an American, my daughter's an American, and I don't want her to be a slave to your damn needs!"

Oskar looked at her with an air of superiority. "What you don't understand, madam, is that your daughter also has needs. But then again," he chuckled, "what would you know of that?"

"I know a lot more than ya think, meathead!" Alice shouted. "Yer nose is bigger than yer brain!" She was now trembling with fury. She raised her arm and pointed to the door. "Git outta my house! I've taken enough of yer shit fer one day!"

Turning, almost clicking his heels, Oskar left. She watched him walk away. Gestapo! A goddamn Nazi, that's what he wuz! Sometin' about that man . . . there wuz sometin' definitely wrong wit him. Still shaking, she reached for a cigarette, lit it with quivering fingers, and flopped down on the couch.

After Oskar's visit, Alice turned to the authorities for help. The social worker had listened as Alice told her story. "I need yer help," she concluded. "Please, I got no one else ta help me . . . make my daughter go ta school. She's really a smart kid, but right now she's a little mixed up."

The social worker promised he would do what he could. He seemed sympathetic and understanding. Confident that everything would be all right, Alice grinned as she walked to the bus stop, pleased with what she had done. When Oskar learned of Alice's petition, he, too, turned to the authorities. He asked the court to appoint him Kathy's legal guardian, promising her a good home complete with mother, father, sister, and brother. He also promised full financial support.

The social worker visited both homes. The house the Kunz family had just bought was on a tree-lined street, with wide sidewalks and well-kept lawns, on the outskirts of Dumont, New Jersey. Though small, the house was immaculately clean and orderly. Peter's sister, Ingrid, was already self-supporting; his mother, Hanna, a seamstress, appeared to be quiet and cooperative.

Next, he visited Alice's apartment in a Brooklyn tenement. It was a hot, muggy June day when he tackled the steps to her walk-up. The hallway was long and dirty. She had washed the faded covers on the couch, stretching them to the linoleum floor, trying to conceal the wooden block that had replaced the missing front leg. She had even washed and starched the curtains on the front windows. She had done her best.

She offered him tea and he accepted. They talked of many things, including the fact that Kathy's father was dead, and that Alice and her children were on welfare. When the social worker left, the children ran after him, waving their good-byes.

* * *

In the courtroom of the family court, dimly lit even on a sunny August day, the judge adjusted his glasses and studied the faces of the two young people before him. They were mere children: the boy, Peter, was seventeen; the girl, Katherine, fifteen. The judge had misgivings, and not only because of their youth. The girl's mother, whom he had met before, walked into the courtroom looking like a whipped dog, her downcast eyes red and swollen. The judge glanced at her small figure with compassion. Life had clearly left its mark on her haggard face; ten illegitimate children, and on welfare. The social worker had recommended the girl's removal from her mother's dirty, noisy and disorderly home. To Alice Jackson's further humiliation, the boy's father, Oskar Kunz, had been appointed Kathy's legal guardian and immediately consented to the marriage.

17

The judge silently beckoned the group closer. Kathy and Peter came to stand directly in front of him. Oskar and Hanna moved to the left, to stand behind Peter. Alice stood alone on the right.

Kathy's black-and-white cotton dress revealed a slim but full-bosomed body. Her low-heeled patent leather shoes reminded the judge of the ones his own granddaughters wore. Kathy's nearsighted brown eyes sparkled at him without a care in the world. Her lips were lightly touched with a pale pink lipstick, but her cheeks needed no color; her clear complexion was flushed with excitement. Her short hair fell in loose ringlets around a fresh, childlike face. There was no question in the judge's mind that she was in love, but was she ready for the responsibilities, the sacrifices and the maturity of marriage? She stood there, waiting for the magic words that would turn her into a loving wife.

Her mother was right, the judge thought, she is a child and should be in school, not getting married. The reports he had read indicated that she was a bright child and had been accepted by the Clara Barton School of Nursing—but that had been before her infatuation with Peter.

Nevertheless, the court had approved the marriage and, like it or not, the judge had a job to do. Still, he hesitated. He looked at the groom, a slender boy whose pale skin contrasted with his dark eyes blazing with candor. Peter stood erect, almost at attention, as though under the gaze of a commanding officer. The judge directed his glance to the boy's father. His manner throughout had been forceful yet persuasive. The voice could be, by turns, harsh or mellow, all heavily tinted with a German accent. His proposal was reasonable. He would support the young couple in his own house for at least five years, while Peter continued his education. His wife would teach Kathy how to make a good home.

Reasonable? Yes, even generous. The judge studied Oskar, trying to figure out what lay behind that high forehead with the dark, receding hair, that large, almost predatory nose, that full mouth. Was it wisdom and kindness—or something else?

Clearing his throat, the judge began.

* * *

Kathy was terrified that something would happen to ruin her plans. Her mother had done everything she could to prevent the marriage. But here she was, with Peter, and the judge was speaking to them. She could tell that the judge didn't approve, but Oskar did, and that was all that mattered. Oskar was a marvelous man. If it hadn't been for his help, she and Peter would not be here now. Oskar had persuaded the social worker. He had a way of making people do what he wanted. He had been like a father to her, the father she had always dreamed of—dignified, clever, commanding, just the opposite of her own father, who, on the few occasions she had seen him, was either drunk or asleep in the hallway, and who was already dead before her eighth birthday. Kathy quickly put it out of her mind as she heard the judge say, "We are gathered here today to join this young man and this woman in the bonds of matrimony." Kathy's heart pounded with excitement; she hardly heard his words, "Katherine Jackson, do you take this man to be your husband?"

"I do, I do!" she wanted to shout, but the judge continued with what sounded like a lot of unnecessary words before he let her answer. She felt Peter's grip tighten on her hand. She turned to look into his eyes as the judge continued with the ceremony. Finally, she heard, "I now pronounce you man and wife." She closed her eyes in disbelief, for a moment did not move, then turned her face up to reach Peter's lips.

Suddenly, there was a loud noise. Alice had started running out of the room. In her headlong departure, her foot had caught the leg of a heavy wooden chair, toppling it and sending it skidding across the waxed floor. Without pausing, Alice pushed her way through the swinging doors, leaving them oscillating wildly. She stopped in the hallway; they could hear her weep. Struck motionless, Kathy stared into Peter's face with troubled, questioning eyes.

"Kiss the bride," Oskar ordered. Peter folded his arms tightly around Kathy's waist, bent his face to hers, and gave her a long, passionate kiss.

In his turn, Oskar kissed the bride, his rough-shaven chin scraping hers as he bestowed a kiss on her almost as intimate as Peter's. Then it was Hanna's turn. At Oskar's command, without much enthusiasm, the sallow, timid woman put her dry, pale lips to Kathy's flushed cheek.

Then there were documents to be signed.

19

"We need your mother's signature, Katherine," the judge said. "I—
" Kathy stammered, "I don't know if she—" The judge understood.

After a few moments of uneasy waiting, Alice appeared, followed
by a court attendant. She had stopped sobbing and looked at them in fury
and despair.

"Will you sign here, please, Mrs. Jackson?" the judge said,
indicating the place in the book and handing her a pen.

Glaring at the judge like a cornered creature, Alice took it, turned
to the book, and whipped around again.

"You'll be sorry for this!" she shouted. Meeting the eyes of each
person in the wedding party, one by one, she repeated, this time in a lower
voice, "You'll be sorry, all of youse."

Turning back to the book, she scrawled her name with such force
that the pen dug into the paper, ripping it.

"We are going to Schrafft's!" Oskar announced, leading the party
out of the courthouse. Alice allowed herself to be dragooned into the
restaurant and sat with the others, eating the ice cream and drinking the
beer. There was little conversation. Kathy and Peter held hands; Oskar
beamed at them paternally. Hanna sat quietly beside her husband, glancing
at him now and then as if to make sure she was doing nothing to displease
him.

As soon as she could, Alice got up.

"I'm goin'," she said, and, without any attempt at good-byes, she
almost ran out of the restaurant. *I did my best, I did my best,* she thought; *I
couldn't do no more.*

Kathy and Peter were married. Worse yet, Kathy was moving to
New Jersey to live under Oskar's brand-new, suburban roof.

As far as Alice was concerned, Kathy would be better off with a
cobra.

CHAPTER 3

1959

Kathy felt transported into another world on a magic carpet floating above the city. Her head on her husband's shoulder, she sat content, silent; just being close to him was enough. She shut her eyes, basking in the warmth of her daydreams.

"We're home, Kathy," Peter said. She opened her eyes and smiled. This was tangible proof that the events of the afternoon had been real. Like a child, she skipped down the tree-lined street, wanting to shout, *we're married! Peter and I are married! Can you believe it?* But she felt Oskar frowning at her. *Control yourself, Katherine,* he seemed to be saying, *you're a married woman now.* He had been so wonderful to her; he had welcomed her so warmly, made her feel so grown up from the first day Peter brought her home.

"This is Kathy," Peter had said.

Oskar had frowned. "Kathy? What kind of name is Kathy? Surely that is not your given name?"

"It's really Katherine, but nobody ever calls me that."

"Katherine," Oskar had sounded delighted. "Now that's a name of substance! I shall call you Katherine."

The memory made her grin at Oskar now, and stop skipping. His approval was important to her.

She tugged at Peter's arm, pulling him close. She took his hand as they walked into the house, their arms swinging like a pendulum measuring off the moments of joy. "Oh, Peter, I'm so happy I want to cry!" Peter smiled and squeezed her hand, yet the look in his eyes was embarrassed, almost haunted.

At the doorstep, they were greeted by a barking dog. Oskar unlocked the front door and led the way in. Kathy stood in the hall, waiting for Peter to proceed downstairs. She knew she was going to share his room. It was not really a room, but part of the basement partitioned off by hanging bamboo strips. Peter called it the "Bamboo Room."

One day a few weeks earlier, she and Peter played hooky from school and went to Dumont for a tour of the Kunz family's new house.

21

The Bamboo Room was big enough only for a dresser and a large double bed with a feather mattress. The mattress had intrigued Kathy from the time she watched Hanna change the bed linens. Peter's mother had plunged her arms deep into the pockets on the sides of the mattress and, with a swift motion, fluffed and lifted the incarcerated feathers till they doubled in size. She had kneaded and punched the soft mass, then covered it with crisp white linens edged with crocheted lace.

On her first visit to the Bamboo Room, Kathy had not been able to resist jumping down on that soft, yielding bed. Peter sat beside her, put his arms around her and kissed her. When his hand stole up her thigh, she pulled away, saying, "No, no, Peter!"

"Why not?" he urged. "Let's make love. If you love me, you'll do it!"

"I do love you, Peter, but I'm afraid, I've never—"

"I know, Kathy, but it's nothing to be afraid of. My father says sex is nothing to be ashamed of. It's a natural expression of love."

"I know, . . . but I'm still afraid."

"Don't be, I won't hurt you," he promised as he began to unbutton her blouse with nervous but eager fingers. She could feel the dampness between her legs as he pushed up her skirt and removed her panties. Suddenly, she felt overwhelmed with desire, and all her fears disappeared.

"Oh, Peter, I love you so much," she whispered. "I'm not afraid anymore. I'm not afraid of anything, as long as you love me."

Peter's fingers found their way into her wet, warm body, searching. Then he began rubbing his hardness against her, back and forth, and she spread her legs wider and wider. Cautiously, almost experimentally, he entered her. He moved slowly, uncertainly. Suddenly, he pushed hard and exploded almost immediately. He moaned like a wounded animal as his body fell limp. Kathy reeled from the suddenness of his thrust and the unexpected pain, but it was over as quickly as it had begun, and left her hanging, at a loss.

Peter hadn't seemed to notice. His body, dripping with sweat, had already rolled to her side, a look of contentment and relief on his face. He reached for her and cradled her in his arms. He loved her, and that was all that mattered.

Now, as Kathy stood in the hallway, a newlywed, thinking of that bed made her feel dizzy, and the color in her cheeks deepened. She was brought back to the present by Oskar's harsh command.

"Why are you standing there, Peter? Take Katherine's bag to your room. Must you wait for me to tell you everything?" He softened his tone as he took Kathy's arm and led her to the kitchen.

"Come, my dear, let's have a beer while Hanna prepares dinner. She's going to make a very special meal tonight."

Kathy glanced back at Peter as he disappeared down the stairs with her almost weightless suitcase. The only item of importance in it was a new, sheer, pale-blue nightgown she had selected with great care for her honeymoon, which would be spent in the Bamboo Room, since Oskar had made it quite clear there was no money for anything else. But Kathy did not mind. Being near Peter was honeymoon enough for her. She would be content just to be his wife and have Oskar and Hanna as a family.

She could hardly contain her excitement as she sat next to Oskar, sipping beer from a can.

"Katherine, my dear," he began in a clear, precise, accent-tinged voice, "now that you are my daughter-in-law, I vill become your teacher. Sometimes, Americans have a difficult time understanding the European vays. Since you are now a part of my family, I vant to help you grow in mind and body. I vill teach you all I know, but you must be a good little girl and listen to me. "I vant to make sure you understand." He patted her gently on her knee and grinned. "Soon my English will be better because you vill teach me your language and I vill teach you love." He lets out a hearty laugh.

"First, you must remember a very important rule—What goes in this house must remain in zis house! Do you understand? Vill you promise to remember that? Kathy nodded silently, as Oskar continued.

"Don't waste time visiting with nosy neighbors and discussing family matters. You vill have more important things to do. Secondly, you know how important it is for Peter to continue his studies. You vill not burden him or me by having babies. No Children while he's in school. Do you understand that?"

23

Kathy only wanted to please. "Oh, Mr. Kunz, I don't want any kids now, I just want to be with Peter. Anyway, Peter's gonna use rubbers." She smiled at his heavily accented reply.

"Good, I'm glad to hear that." Oskar hitched his broad wooden captain's chair closer, his voice shifting again, becoming more and more confidential. "Now that you are my daughter-in-law, Katherine, you may call me Oskar. I vant you to think of me as a friend and confidant. Come to me with your problems, not to Peter. His mind must be kept on his studies."

She nodded, not knowing quite what to say. It seemed odd for Oskar to ask that.

He went on, his eyes fixed on hers. "We vill have long talks, you and I, and we vill become close friends. I vill take care of you and Peter for the next few years, and you in turn vill take care of me and help Hanna with the house."

Peter entered and joined them at the table. Kathy reached for him and threw her arms around his neck.

"Oh Peter, I'm so lucky," she cried, pushing aside the twinge of misgiving. "Your parents are so great. I never knew a family like this before. How lucky I am to have found you." She turned to Oskar. "All of you." She reached for Oskar, kissed him lightly on the cheek.

"Love is a wonderful thing, Katherine. It's meant to be shared. That is something I have always taught my family."

Oskar seemingly satisfied with Kathy's attention suddenly called to his wife, "Hanna, what is taking you so long? Can't you see we are all starving?"

Kathy helped Hanna set the table, handling the matching dishes with a pleasure bordering on reverence. Peter was sent to fetch a bottle of wine from the basement. Delicious smells perfumed the air. Hanna had prepared Oskar's favorite, turtle soup, and *roulade* with red cabbage, *knodl*, and peas. There was a side dish of celery *salati* with sour cream. Kathy eyed the strange, delectable-looking foods with eagerness while Peter poured the wine.

"It is too bad Ingrid can't be here today." Oskar said, "She's still on her honeymoon. If she were here, I am sure she would join us in a toast to the newlyweds. *Zum Wohle!*" he shouted, holding his glass high.

24

"Zum Wohle" Peter and Hanna echoed.

"Cheers"! Kathy smiled as they all clinked glasses. Never before had she been a part of anything that even faintly resembled such a celebration.

She ate very little, so filled with happiness and gratitude that there seemed hardly any room left for food. She began to long for the evening to be over so that she and Peter could be alone in the Bamboo Room.

She dutifully helped Hanna clear away the dishes.

Oskar and Pete stayed at the table, Oskar talking and Peter listening. When Kathy rejoined them, Hanna brought out cognac glasses. Kathy had never even heard of cognac, but Oskar insisted that she taste it and laughed as she choked on her first sip.

"More, more," he urged. "It's good for you. It will make your blood hot!" Kathy took a few more sips but preferred the hazelnut crème tarts that Hanna served for dessert. *After this,* Kathy thought, *I wish Peter and I could leave.* As if reading her mind, Oskar put a restraining hand on her arm.

"Now, my dear, I have important matters to discuss with you." He took a sip of his cognac. "Although it is important to develop your body, your mind must be cultivated as well. In order for me to help you, Katherine, I must know vat you are thinking. The only vay I will know that is if you write your thoughts on paper for me to read. I have always taught my children to write everything down, and I would like you to do the same. Vill you do that for me, please?"

His smile was warm, but his request confused her. It seemed odd—but not at odds with the strangeness of his earlier request. Her gut feeling was to say no. But, instead said, "What— What do you want me to write?"

"Anything . . . anything that comes to your mind."

"Like what? I don't know what you mean."

"Well, tell me what you are feeling at this moment."

"Happy. That's an easy question. I feel very happy. I feel so much love for all of you. I just feel happy. That's all I can say."

"And that is enough," he said. "That is what I want you to write."

Hanna got up, found paper and pencil, and placed them before Kathy. It seemed a funny thing to do on one's wedding night, but there was no pain in it, so Kathy obediently wrote the short sentences, pushing the paper over to Oskar when she finished.

"Tomorrow you vill write a little more, and the next day and the next, until before long you'll be writing inner thoughts which you'll be surprised you ever possessed."

He turned to Hanna. "Get me my book. I vant to read some of my writings to Katherine."

Within minutes, Hanna returned with a large loose-leaf notebook and handed it to her husband. Oskar opened it, studied it briefly, cleared his throat, and began to read:

"The one thing I can miss most in a human being is intelligence. Vonderful to possess it, vonderful to witness it, but it is not an achievement in itself. I could hardly stand it if anybody were much better than I in these points: to try to be just vith reason, to be tolerant vith only one exception—against intolerance, to be vividly interested, and to be able to love and accept love. What I easily can miss besides these points are: perfection, infallibility, and the talk about them. What I can't stand: deadly seriousness in anything. I hate small hearts—and mediocrity."

Oskar closed the book and smiled at Kathy, seemingly pleased with the passage he had chosen to read.

"Do you see what I mean, Katherine? I vant you to tell me what you think, how you feel, what you believe in. Vill you do that for me?"

Kathy smiled back. "I don't know if I can, but I'll try."

"Good. I can help you a great deal, but only if I know what you are thinking. Do you understand that?"

"I think so."

"Good. All right, Peter, I guess it's time. You may take your bride to bed now but remember what I told you."

Kathy jumped up from the table, reached for Peter's hand, and pulled him from his chair. When she heard him say good night, she blurted out a hurried goodnight of her own but continued to tug on him. Like children, they ran out of the kitchen and skipped down the stairs, soon to fall into the soft, fluffy, feathery heaven she had dreamed about.

Peter held the bamboo dividers open, allowing her to enter. She took one step into the room, stopped, and turned to look at her husband, bewildered.

26

"Peter, where's the big bed?" For there, before her, was a small single bed with no legs, lying in the middle of the sparsely furnished room, covered only with a faded brown bedspread. "Where is the feather bed?" He seemed surprised that she remembered it. "My parents have it in their bedroom. Their bed is in the attic now. We fixed a room up there for my grandmother. She's coming to visit soon. This bed was Ingrid's, but now that she's married, I get to have it."

"Oh," Kathy said, trying to banish her disappointment.

Peter reached for her and began kissing her neck. "What difference does it make? A bed's a bed. It's what we do in it that matters." He nibbled gently at her earlobe and whispered, "I love you, Mrs. Kunz. May I have the pleasure of undressing you?"

"No, you may not." She giggled, pushing him aside. "I have a surprise for you. Close your eyes. Please."

"Close my eyes? What for? I want to look at you."

"You will Peter, in a few minutes. Please don't peek. I'll tell you when to open them."

Feigning anger, Peter grunted and flopped on the mattress. He did not close his eyes but began removing his shoes and socks. Kathy ran to her suitcase and opened it. Turning her back to him, she stripped off her dress. She thought she heard the creaking of a stair, and looked up, but hearing nothing further, continued disrobing. Still with her back to Peter, she asked teasingly, "You're not peeking, are you?"

"No, but if you don't hurry up, I will." He jumped from the bed, grabbed her waist, and pulled her close.

"Peter, you promised. I wanted you to see my new nightgown."

"I'd rather see your body," he said huskily.

"No," she cried, "you'll spoil it! I want to first show you my gown!" She picked up a pillow and threw it at him. The spirited pillow fight that ensued for the next few minutes left the bed covers in shambles. Weak with laughter and out of breath, they rolled to the floor. Suddenly startled by the clatter of the bamboo strips, they looked up to see Oskar looming over them. Kathy reached frantically for the covers but couldn't pull them from beneath Peter. She scampered behind him and drew her knees up to her chin, clasping her arms around them for cover. Pete seemed startled, yet undisturbed. He looked up at his father.

"Yes, father? Do you want something?"

Oskar looked around the room and replied gravely, "I vant to remind you of vat ve discussed this evening."

"Don't worry," Peter replied with a smile, "I'll be careful."

Oskar turned and walked from the room, the bamboo strips clattering softly behind him.

Kathy's face was flushed with embarrassment; discomfited yet again by the man's odd behavior, she hardly knew where to begin.

"Peter, does your father always walk in unannounced? I mean . . . I have no clothes on!"

"Oh, you'll get used to him. Things like that don't bother him. He probably didn't even notice you. He's just worried that I might get you pregnant, that's all."

"I know. He talked to me about it earlier today. I told him you were going to use rubbers."

Peter shrugged and walked to the dresser. "Forget it, honey, we've got more important things to think about right now."

He's right, Kathy thought as she jumped up from the floor. *He has to be.* She had made her choice, that much she knew; she—they—would see it was the right one. And nothing was going to spoil this night. It was their night, Peter's and hers. She reached for her gown and quickly pulled it over her head, ironing out the wrinkles with her hands. Its softness made her feel sexy. Her body shivered with excitement as she whirled about the room. "I feel like Cinderella going to her first ball."

Peter turned and stared. "Honey, you look delicious."

Gently, he took her in his arms and kissed her.

"Pinch me, Peter, and tell me it's not all a dream."

He grabbed her behind, roughly lifted her into the air, and spun her furiously in a circle. Kathy squealed with delight as he dropped her on the mattress, her head still spinning. Then, with a dramatic bow, Peter leaned forward and said in an exaggerated German accent, "Now, dear madam, if you will allow me to undress, I may have something of interest for you."

He pulled her on top of him and began caressing her, moving his body in rhythmic motions beneath her. She kissed him hard, returning the passion she felt radiating from his body. Turning her on her back, Peter began to probe her ears with his wet tongue, kissing her neck. Kathy was enjoying the new sensations and wanted to watch as he made his way down her body. She pulled a pillow under her head, her eyes wide with anticipation, her lips slightly parted. He was kissing her breasts now, causing the nipples to harden. She whimpered. He began sucking, more aggressively, almost biting her breasts, and a sharp pain broke her euphoric spell. Protectively, she raised her hand and pushed his face away, gently rubbing her sore nipples with the palm of her hand. Peter seemed fascinated by her movements, and his arousal grew. She felt him spread her legs and push to enter her. She felt his hard, pulsating penis move deeper and deeper inside, in fast, rhythmic movements. "Are you ready?" she heard him whisper. Without waiting for a response, Peter moaned loudly, "I'm coming, honey, I'm coming," and within seconds fell limp.

Kathy held on to him, kissing his sweaty face. "Oh, Peter, I love you so much. Please don't stop. I want to love you some more."

Languidly, Peter rolled to her side and stretched his body. "I love you too, Kathy."

She sat up quickly and threw herself across his chest, covering it with kisses. "Please, Peter, love me some more?"

He cupped her face in his hands and lightly brushed her lips with his. "I will, honey, as soon as I catch my breath." Within minutes, he was snoring.

Kathy stayed awake for a long time, nibbling her lower lip. She had expected more. But then, she thought, perhaps there were many things, as Oskar had advised her, that as an American she simply didn't understand about the European ways. That was only natural, she told herself. At least she had what she wanted. Their plan had succeeded. At least there was that.

A secret smile curled in the corner of her mouth as she studied her sleeping prince. She counted the hairs on his chest. She noted that his pubic hair was light and sparse. She gently stroked his body, careful not to awaken him, and sighed, resting her head on Peter's shoulder, her neck in the crook of his arm, where she finally fell asleep.

CHAPTER 4

1960

Kathy awoke one April morning, no longer startled to find her father-in-law standing over her bed. "Good morning, Oskar," she said cheerfully, poking her arm out from under the covers as she yawned and stretched luxuriously. "What time is it?"

"Nine o'clock."

"Oh gosh, I didn't intend to sleep that late. Can I get you something, Oskar?"

"No, I've already had breakfast, but Oma hasn't come down yet. Why don't you take breakfast up to her?"

"Sure, sure." Kathy hopped out of bed and into her robe and slippers. She quickly walked up the stairs, with Oskar bringing up the rear. He sat at the kitchen table, sipping coffee, smoking a cigarette, while Kathy prepared breakfast for his mother-in-law. Oma had been living with them for almost six months now, in the spare room in the attic. She spoke no English, made no attempt to be friendly and Kathy had a hard time trying to communicate with her.

She took the eggs out of the icebox and cracked them into a frying pan. The grease sizzled and spat at her as she dropped them in, one at a time. Oskar watched silently. Lately, she had become more aware of his stares. She had mentioned to Peter that he made her nervous and she felt as if she were under his constant surveillance.

"It's because he wants to help you," Peter had explained. "You have a tendency to be too frivolous and too spirited. He says you have a good mind, but it needs cultivating. Remember what I told you about my father. He's very smart and whatever he does, it's always in our best interest. Just do what father says, and we'll both stay out of trouble." Peter had placed a kiss on her cheek, dispelling for the moment, the anxiety that had come to occupy a place in her young mind.

The sound of the popping toaster startled her for the moment, and she jumped back. "Darn, that scared me!" she said.

Oskar laughed. "Sometimes I wonder how I lived without you. You are the only one with any life, around here. You are like a puppy at

30

play. When I compare you with Hanna, I feel cheated. She does nothing but sit and sew all evening."

"Oh, Oskar, stop! Hanna works hard all day and when she gets home, she's tired. What do you want her to do—a jig?"

"That would be a sight, wouldn't it?" Oskar smiled. "She is too old and fat for that now, but when she was young, she was a good dancer. Did Peter ever tell you his mother was in show business in Germany?"

"Show business? No, he never told me that."

Not for the first time, Kathy felt sorry for Hanna. To have been in the glamorous world of the theater once, and now . . . "I'd never have guessed," she admitted.

"It's true. She was very pretty. But never as pretty as you, Katherine." She ignored his comment. She stood with her back to him, putting the eggs on the plate. "Do you think Oma wants jelly?"

Suddenly, she felt his warm breath on her neck. She turned quickly, almost dropping the plate. "Oh, I'm sorry."

"Let me help you," he said, taking the plate from her. She moved quickly, reaching for the tray on top of the refrigerator, holding it like a shield, a barrier between them.

"If you get the coffee, I'll take the tray up to Oma," Kathy replied, wondering why she felt compelled to get out of the room as quickly as she could. Oskar seemed to take pleasure in her discomfort.

He poured the coffee. "Here you are, Katherine. It's ready to go."

Kathy went upstairs and with her foot, pushed open the door of the tiny attic room. Oma sat in the bed, waiting, her white hair spilling over the shoulders of her pink wool bed jacket, regarding Kathy with small, suspicious eyes.

"Here it is, Oma," Kathy said cheerfully, knowing she would get no answer. *I don't know why she hates me,* Kathy thought, *but it doesn't matter, I don't like her much either.*

She arranged the tray carefully in front of the old woman, then, without saying good-bye, went back to her room to get dressed. The basement was dark, but the radio was playing, and she realized that Oskar was in his workshop, listening to the music. He had recently quit his job at the electronics factory and set up his own business, making special-function integrated circuits. Peter thought his father was a genius and bragged that he had several patents pending.

Kathy dressed in the semi-darkness and brushed her hair. She was about to go back upstairs when Oskar called to her.

"Would you like to see an album of Hanna when she was in show biz?"

"All right, but it's so dark in here, I don't know how you can see anything, unless you're a bat." As she walked in, Kathy pulled the string of the overhead light. It flickered momentarily, then lit up the room. A workbench stood in one corner, cluttered with tools of every size. Separate piles of finished and unfinished units were neatly stacked on shelves on the wall. Oskar, looking quite comfortable, sat in an overstuffed chair in the corner of the room, his feet resting on a well-worn hassock.

"Now, that's better." Kathy said. "At least I can see something."

"Take a seat," he said, motioning to the hassock. He handed her an album with a tattered leather cover and moved behind her. "You don't need light to enjoy good music, Katherine. Relax! That's the trouble with you American girls, you don't know how to relax. It's very healthy for your body, you know." He began massaging the muscles of her neck.

"How does that feel? Nice, huh? Did Peter ever tell you that you have a beautiful body?"

"Oh, Oskar, stop, you're making me blush." She jumped off the hassock and put the album down. "I can look at this later. I think we should go outside. It's such a beautiful day."

Oskar agreed. Together, they walked into the sunshine. The crocuses were budding along the pathways. Robins searched the lawn for worms.

The yard was not large, but the thickly planted scrub allowed complete privacy. Large pine trees lined the side of the house, obscuring any view of the neighboring homes.

Oskar had taken King, the German shepherd, with them and the dog ran wildly through the grass. Oskar picked up a stick and threw it high into the sky. King ran in rapid pursuit. He retrieved it over and over again. Oskar finally sat on the grass in the shade, pulling Kathy beside him.

"Katherine," he began, "I must tell you something that has been disturbing me." She knew she was in for another lecture. "Your writings are beginning to upset me. Don't misunderstand me, you write very well, my dear, but your desire to visit with the neighbors, for instance, is upsetting. You really shouldn't think of things like that—it can only cause trouble. You must realize that when our neighbor, Ruth, invites you for coffee, it is not because she's fond of you, it's because she's nosy and wants to pry into our family business." He kissed the top of her head and continued, "Are you listening to me, Katherine? I know what I'm talking about. When you get lonely don't talk to the neighbors, talk to me." He picked up her hand and held it for a moment, caressing it gently. His voice was sincere. "I want to be your friend, your best friend, if you will let me. Will you give me that chance?" He tilted her chin. "Yes?"

Kathy nodded.

"If you feel sad and want to talk, I am here for you. And, before you get any more of those silly Brooklyn ideas," Oskar chuckled, "talk to me. Okay? All I want is your happiness. You do believe that, don't you, Katherine?" Again, she nodded. "Will you promise to share your thoughts with me?"

"I'm sorry, Oskar, I'm really very happy here, but . . . it's just that sometimes I want to talk to other people. I have no friends and I haven't seen my mother in a long time."

"You have *no need* to see her." The gentleness vanished from his voice. "She is a stubborn old woman, and you're better off without her."

"Don't say that, Oskar. She's still my mother, and I do love her, you know."

"Love?" His tone had a cutting edge to it. "What do you know of love? Every child loves her mother, but you have much to learn of real love. There are many kinds of love you know."

"I know that" She smiled.

"Don't ever look for love. It's not anything you can look for. So many people don't know that because they feel they need it so badly. It's never beside you: it is always inside you. That is why you recognize it when it comes. Do you understand me, child?"

"Yes, of course, Oskar." Kathy was getting defensive. "Peter and I have…"

"You and Peter are still teenagers. You know nothing of love, but you will learn. You must always love something, and if there is nobody around to love, you will love an insect, or maybe a pebble in your path. I don't think the sun could survive if it had to keep all its warmth to itself. I once read: You are as deeply in love with others as you are in yourself. It must be true. The more you are able to feel for others, the more you are able to be hurt. If water meets water, it will flow together. If you're not near water, you have no possibility of flowing. You can only be absorbed or swept away. And you'll never know anything else." He paused, as if in thought.

"When there is love, you'll know it," he assured her. "If there is love, you can never escape it, even if you want to. Most people are dumb and scared when it comes to affairs of the heart. Just believe in it. Believe in your own heart. It has to be ready. Do you understand anything of what I am trying to say, Katherine?"

"Yes, Oskar, I do. That's the way I feel about Peter. I would do anything for him. I..."

Again, Oskar interrupted. "You must do everything for him, Katherine. It is your duty, your responsibility as a wife. You must always obey your husband and me. We want to protect you because we love you. You and Peter are my responsibility, and, because of my love for him, I have taken on the added burden of supporting you. Do you realize how much it costs just to feed and clothe you, not to mention the cost of his school? It hasn't been easy, you know."

"I know, Oskar, and I'm sorry. I don't mean to be ungrateful. I'm really sorry. I guess I'm like my mother, a stubborn old...."

"You are not old, Katherine." He smiled. "Stubborn, yes, but beautiful." He stood up and extended his hand to her, helping her up on her feet. There was an almost eerie certainty in his touch, overpowering, absolute.

"It is permissible for you to express an opinion, Katherine," Oskar went on as they walked, "but when I show you that you are wrong, you mustn't continue to argue. You must accept my views and change your way of thinking. Remember, I have your best interest in mind. I have a lot of patience, and I have grown very fond of you, so I will teach you all that I know. You have become a real part of my life, more than you realize, and you must let me become a part of yours. I am not so old, you know, that I do not have needs also."

34

King persisted in his pursuit of the stick, and Oskar finally threw it again, laughing at the dog's determination and enthusiasm.

"This dog needs no one but me, Katherine. Perhaps, someday, you will feel the same way."

Kathy felt tears in her eyes. She was unsure whether they were of fear or guilt. She was growing accustomed to Oskar's strange European ways. She was also growing accustomed to being cared for. She had never known such strength, or such concern. Perhaps she didn't need to guard herself from Oskar with such exhausting vigilance.

"Oskar, you always make me feel so guilty, so unappreciative of everything you do for me. I don't know what my life would have been if you hadn't let Peter and me marry. I could never have asked for a better father. I'm sorry I've offended you. I promise not to argue with you anymore. Sometimes I'm so stupid."

"No, no, my dear, you're not stupid, just young. You'll learn to be patient." He lifted her chin. "Now, let me see that beautiful smile. It's too lovely a day for tears. Come, let us lie in the sun."

Oskar removed his shirt and undershirt, revealing his bare chest. He lay back on the grass, his hands clasped behind his head. Kathy looked at him. It's amazing, she thought, how different a father and son can be. Oskar's chest was a mass of black hair, while Peter's was almost bare. Oskar had a strong, well-built look, but his legs were too short for his body. Peter was better proportioned.

"What are you looking at? Oskar asked with a laugh. "Haven't you ever seen a hairy chest before?"

"I just noticed that mark under your arm." She reached over and touched it. "When did you get that? I never knew you had a tattoo."

"There are a lot of things you don't know about me, Katherine." He rubbed his hand over it, as if remembering.

"It's *O* for *Oskar*. It's been there many years, more years than I care to remember." He reached over and pulled her closer. "Come, lay back. The sun feels so wonderful; or perhaps it's you who makes me feel so warm."

Kathy was pleased that her father-in-law had a genuine feeling of love for her. "Oh, Oskar, I wish I could express my feelings like…"

"Some people are poor with words," he declared. "Others can express their deepest thoughts quite easily. Sometimes, my dear Katherine, a simple gesture of the hand, a look of the human eye, a slight touch—like stroking your hand in sympathy over the hair of another person— can say much more than a spoken word. Some people would resent this touch, because they have erected barriers that make it impossible for them to agree to this way of communication."

King came to a running halt before them, again dropping the stick at his master's feet. Oskar picked it up and held it. The dog sat, ears erect, waiting.

"Do you see how this dog is communicating with me? It's just a question of giving and receiving. Isn't that the motive behind every communication? In the end, isn't that all anyone, animals and humans alike, can do—give and receive?"

"I hadn't thought about it that way, Oskar, but I guess you're right."

He reached out to stroke her arm with the back of his fingers, neither pausing to squeeze her flesh nor proceeding to greater intimacies.

"If you listen, you can clearly see what I resent: the fact that anybody can be cut down by definite rules and regulations. This is an infringement on our personal freedom. Sex, in this sense, is for sure the deepest, most meaningful way of communicating between two human beings. But—" he paused and raised himself to lean on his elbow— "this is taken as the reason to limit this form of communication to one single person, at least one at a time." He chuckled. "You get to choose one forever. What a dishonest farce!"

"I only want one forever!" Kathy cried. "I don't need anyone else but Peter."

Oskar shook his head. "What a depressing view of two human beings. Do you realize that you cut yourself down so much, excluding yourself from something that would make you recognize and understand human beings? It would let you gain the very things that we are all starving for: acceptance, personal growth, and an overcoming of the basic loneliness you were just talking about."

He stood up and extended his hand to her. Together, they began to walk through the garden.

"Oh yes, I know some big guys who are proud of their strengths in loneliness and, consequently, their independence, but it turns my stomach when I see their pride in their masculinity. Did you ever think how they claim that right for the one person they choose, but deny it for every other person, no matter what his personality should be? Did you ever think of that?"

"No, I'm not sure I even understand it."

"You will, my dear. You are still young and have much to learn. Being a male, I know what kind of suspicion I provoke. I must be after sex, as most males are, although . . . that is not my personal opinion. Certain things cannot be changed and just have to be accepted." He stopped and looked at her. "I hope you do not think from what I have said that I am advocating free love. Oh, no! I believe that love should be free; it should be natural. Of course, Katherine, this does not mean I want to indulge in love at any given opportunity. The questions seem to be quite reversed: love is cut down to a very restricted area. From this side comes regulations and pressure. The other side always yells, 'He advocates a free-for-all!'—if one resents that this pressure is applied.

"Now, if I were a female like you, Katherine, I would be on the other end of the scale. You, my dear, must always be on constant guard against this male attitude, the almost born-in concept that can't be shaken. I believe, from time to time, we should reevaluate the established theory. This is the only way for progress. Don't you agree, Katherine?"

She nodded, not quite understanding, but his tone was so strong, so believable, she was sure he must be right.

Oskar picked up the stick and held it to King's nose. "Do you see how he waits for me? Look at his eye, so loyal, so loving. It is the way the world should be, but . . . human history shows over and over, in every category of human interest, how theories one got 'used to,' are held up and cherished so much that there is every kind of imaginable refusal to look at any facts, no matter how accessible. Whoever may have originally invented the notion of sex as being sacred, forbidden, restricted to one specific person, something dirty one way or another, something of reward or final giving in to commensurate efforts—must have been a very mediocre or at least superficial personality. Being motivated by the wish to have a full giving or receiving of sex, only between two chosen or contracted people, is so limited an outlook on life, so far from being a grown personality, that one may wonder how almost everybody subscribes to it."

Oskar threw the stick into the bushes, with King in full pursuit.

"You know, Katherine, it is beyond me how human beings can cut down themselves, their own personalities to such a small size, to adjust to one single other person, as if that, from now on, constituted for them the content of the universe. It is a ridiculous thought: that's all one wants to offer to the contracted person, to the person one pretends to love and for whom one wants as much as possible? What is especially beyond me is, how *that* could have been made into some principle of high moral standards everybody feels so self-righteous with. A complete twist to consider self-limiting and limiting others as moral achievement, backed up by wonderful ideals like chastity, virginity . . . But it is a well-known twist, admirably performed by many religions."

"Oskar?" Kathy interrupted. "Are you an atheist?"

"Who, me?" He guffawed. "What would ever give you that idea? Religions don't strive for personalities, they strive for unification, stressing the belief in the last letter of their scriptures by everybody.

"A person like that—if he is serious—will in all probability never know what advantages were near him, which he walked by with closed eyes. But he must know, somehow, deep down in himself. In fact, this is all his fear. These contracts are nothing else but reassurances between two moral cowards, that such a thing shall never happen. Each one of the two is too weak morally and feels too inferior to let the other one eventually aspire to something, or eventually to look up to themselves. One just has to look at the disgusting view, how they watch their contracts against infringements. There is often not much left of human decency and trust, not even in the maturity of another person, to sign such a contract.

"Do you know what the problem in our society is?"

Kathy didn't understand any of what he was talking about but felt deeply flattered that he, a man of the world, would talk to her so seriously. "No, I don't think I do."

"The whole problem looks to me to be a question of sincere, upright, and decent behavior toward facts and situations, in short, toward life. If people could see that, if they wanted to learn to look at things unprejudiced and with a sincere heart and without their own personal wishes involved, yes, if they all wanted to learn that. . . I would be convinced that in such a state of mind and character, there would never be another way possible. It's the attitude that's wrong, and we can't hinder a wrong thing from happening.

"I hope, dear Katherine, that you have not misunderstood my words. I hope that you do not read into my words that I am saying love could achieve that. Love can do as much wrong as hate. Hate does not have to have more negative value than love. In fact, it can have as much positive value as love. Too weak a hate for certain situations cannot yield enough seriousness to cope with problems, just as too little love cannot. Honesty and upright care give more than love and hate, because only they can lead to love and hate. Only those, who care sincerely and honestly for everything, do not have to worry about love and hate. They will find them . . . feel them . . . and live with them in a harmonious and happy life. That, my dear Katherine, is what you and I will do: live a harmonious and happy life together."

CHAPTER 5

1960

That evening, the Bamboo Room felt hotter and stuffier than usual. Kathy perched on the edge of the bed, picked up her pad and pencil, and began to write down her thoughts, which by now had become a nightly ritual.

HURRY HOME PETER, I MISS YOU. IT'S SO DAMN HOT IN HERE. NEED SOME FRESH AIR. HAD A NICE TALK TODAY WITH OSKAR. A LOT I DON'T UNDERSTAND. WE'RE GOING TO TALK MORE.

The bamboo strips rustled as Peter, rumpled and sweaty, entered the room. "Hi, honey." He leaned over and pecked her on the cheek. "What are you doing down here on such a hot night?"

"I was waiting for you. I was just writing a poem about King. We had such a great time in the yard this afternoon. Do you want to hear my poem?"

"Sure. Read it while I get undressed. I don't know how you stay in this room. It's so hot! Let's take a walk outside, it's got to be cooler out there."

"Good idea," she said, jumping from the bed. "But first, you have to hear my poem:
Out he jumps to get his stick
For you to throw with one fast flick
So he can chase with all his might
And bring it back for you
Again to throw it out of sight"
Peter smiled. "It's pretty good, for a beginner. C'mon." He grabbed her playfully around the waist. "Let's get out of this sweat box."

Dressed in their robes, they tiptoed up the stairs, careful not to disturb Oskar and Hanna.

The air outside was cool, the waxing moon bright. Kathy led him by the hand to a big willow tree and slipped off her robe. She stood before him nude, her breasts casting faint shadows on her body.

She whispered, "Come on, honey, let's make love."

In the moonlight, Peter's face glowed, his eyes devouring her body. He reached for her, and together they slid to the grass.

Kathy aggressively rolled Peter over on his back, kissing him hungrily. She tugged at his belt, the robe opened; then, freeing his arms, he pulled it off, converted it into a blanket. She had waited for this all afternoon. She smothered his face with kisses, pushing her tongue deep into his mouth, her body on fire. Overwhelmed by her passion, Kathy trapped him between her legs, moving rhythmically. She lifted her chest, allowing the evening breeze to fondle her breasts. Peter tried to pull her closer, but she resisted, wanting only his tongue to caress her body.

Soon she wanted more. She wanted to feel him deep in her body. She mounted him; his penis wrapped in her warmth. Peter moaned.

"Ohhh, Kathy!" His thrusts threw her into a crescendo of sensations she had never felt before.

"Oh, Peter, I love you so much." They clung to each other for a long time. This was a moment to savor, a moment unlike any other she had ever known.

* * *

The weeks passed quickly, and the summer heat began. Kathy rose early one morning and began to dress. She stood in front of the mirror and rubbed her breasts. She realized, as she put on her bra, that they seemed larger and were constantly sore. Peter, absorbed in a book, lay on the bed, propped between two pillows.

"Peter," she began disjointedly, "do you. . . I mean, how can you tell if . . . ah, what I'm trying to say is…" she hesitated, trying to get his attention. "Peter, you're not *listening* to me!"

Without taking his eyes off the book, he replied, "I'm listening, but you haven't said anything yet."

41

"Oh, Peter," she blurted out, as she lay next to him and buried her head in his shoulder, "what I'm trying to say is, how do you really know if you're pregnant?"

She could feel her husband stiffen as he pulled himself upright on the bed.

"Did . . . did you miss your period?" he asked, somewhat timidly.

"Yes."

"How many?"

"Almost two."

"What do you mean, almost two?" He was getting impatient.

She began to sob. "I really only missed one, but I'm due now and I guess I'm late again . . . Peter, I'm afraid. I'm just not sure. How are you supposed to know?" She started to tremble.

"Shush," he whispered. He kissed the top of her head, stroking her hair. "Don't worry, honey, my father will know what to do. He always knows what to do. Everything will be all right. Come," he said as he rose from the bed, "we must go and tell father."

"Wait, Peter, maybe we shouldn't tell him just yet. Maybe we should wait a little longer. Maybe I'm not really pregnant, just a little late."

"No, Kathy, we can't wait. The sooner we tell him, the better. We did make a promise, you know."

"Yes, I know, Peter," she said solemnly. "But I don't want to tell him. You tell him."

The bamboo strips swung back and forth as Peter left the room. It was so hot the air felt heavy, foul from the lack of ventilation. At times like those, in the windowless room, a feeling of claustrophobia often overcame her, but this was different. The fear of what might come next was choking her. She thought of her mother and wondered what she would do if she were there. Kathy hadn't seen her mother since her wedding day. She invited her to the house, more than once, but Alice's reply had remained the same.

"Yah know where I live. I'm not comin' nowhere near that house with that crazy man there." Kathy could never understand her mother's hatred of Oskar. She thought perhaps Alice had grown jealous of the warm bond that had developed between them. Her thoughts were interrupted by Oskar's voice.

It sounded like a whip.

"Katherine, come up here!"

She jumped from the bed and ran up the stairs. Oskar and Peter were sitting at the kitchen table. Oskar glared at her. Peter looked away. She walked past Hanna, who stood at the sink, noisily scrubbing a large pot. Their eyes met briefly, but they did not speak. Oskar fingered a half-empty bottle of beer; a full mug sat in front of him. As she walked past him, he suddenly reached out and grabbed her arm. Shaking his forefinger at her, he growled, "You are a disobedient child. I told you there would be no babies in this house until Peter finished school."

Kathy saw a look in his eyes she had never seen before.

"You Americans can't be trusted!" he shouted. "Your word means *nothing*!" The more he spoke, the angrier he became. "Did I not tell you no babies, huh? Why did you not listen?"

"I'm sorry, Oskar," she began. Suddenly his hand slashed across her face. Kathy's eyes opened wide in disbelief.

"I didn't *mean* to," she whimpered. "I really didn't. I don't even know for sure if I am pregnant."

He grabbed her shoulders and began to shake her. "Why did you not tell me sooner? Were you trying to keep it from me?"

"No, honest, I just didn't know for sure. I still don't."

"What do you mean, you didn't know? What's there to know? I told you to tell me everything. Everything, do you understand!"

"I told Peter."

"Not Peter," Oskar shouted, "*me!* I told you to tell *me*."

Kathy tore herself from his grip and ran to Peter, half of her face ablaze. She wrapped her arms around her husband, crying, "Peter, please! Do something!"

She shivered when she saw his cold, expressionless face. He pushed her away.

"My father will make the decision, Kathy. It's up to him."

"It's always up to me," said Oskar, glaring at his son and daughter-in-law. "This family cannot survive without me. I have to make all the decisions around here. Look at them—" he turned to his wife, waving his arms in their direction. "There isn't a brain between them. They couldn't make a decision if their life depended upon it. But you, dear Katherine," he said bitingly, fixing her with a white fury in his eyes, "you—you *must* learn not to question my decisions. You promised there would be no children, and your word is very important. So . . ." He eyeballed her. "My dear disobedient daughter-in-law, you must have an abortion."

"Oh no!" she pleaded, horrified. This was exactly what she hoped beyond hope he would not say. "Please, Oskar, I'll do anything you say, but let me have this baby. We've been married almost a year now."

"You will not have a baby, Katherine! I can't afford to feed another mouth, and that's final!"

"But . . . you can't. Please, Oskar, please."

He continued to fix her with his glare. "Human life is not a bit more precious than any other life, even a worm's. It all depends on what is done with that life. If there is an ape who does not invent an H-bomb for the purpose of dropping it on anything, his life is worth more than that of a human being who invents it for that purpose."

"It's not an ape!" Kathy screamed. "It's my baby! Oh God, Oskar, isn't your grandchild's life worth anything?"

Oskar clamped his teeth together in a scowl, his jaw muscles working. "It's a Christian construct, to put a fixed value on human life," he said. "We pay dearly for our arrogance to consider us as the children of some god. Are only we his children—all others his creatures? Did anybody ever ask him if he really meant it this way? The worst thing of all bad things is to put a fixed value on anything. For Christ's sake, even syphilis can do some good, if it befalls the right person—like one of the popes!"

Kathy turned to Peter, her eyes pleading for help, but he would not look at her. She reached for his hand. "Peter, please, do something. Don't just sit there, *help* me!"

After an awkward silence, Peter spoke up. He rubbed his thumb over his fingernails as he spoke, and seemed perturbed, almost offended, his eyes flat, his face a flaccid mask. "Kathy please do what my father says. He knows what's best for us." His voice had a hollow edge to it. "We can have children later. You must listen to him and let him perform an abortion."

44

"*Him?* What do you mean, *let him perform an abortion?* Kathy's eyes searched the room wildly, looking for help.

No one spoke. Hanna turned back to the sink, still scrubbing the same pot. Peter waited for Oskar's next move. Oskar took his time and seemed to enjoy the heavy silence. He looked down at his empty mug and beckoned Hanna for a refill. Anxiously, she reached into the icebox for another beer and quietly placed it before him.

Finally, Oskar spoke, his voice now deadly calm. "My child, you have nothing to fear from me. I am going to help you. I have performed abortions many times."

"How could you perform abortions? You're not a doctor!"

"One need not be a doctor to perform abortions. One must only have intelligence." Lifting his mug to his mouth, Oskar sucked noisily on his beer, a line of foam forming on his upper lip. "It really is very easy once you know how. I learned many years ago in Germany."

Kathy stared at him and at all of them, unbelieving. A choked scream rose in her throat. She ran around the kitchen table, shouting wildly, deliberately knocking over a wooden chair, which crashed noisily to the floor.

"Well, this is not Germany. This is *America*! Abortion is illegal!" She ran from the room in tears.

"Honey, wait!" cried Peter.

Blindly, she almost tumbled down the stairs. She grappled with the bamboo strips as she entered their bedroom, angrily pulling them from their bindings, leaving a gaping hole. She threw herself on the bed. *No one's going to talk me into this,* she thought, *no matter how much logic they use. Besides, I know it's illegal. He can't do this, he just can't!* She heard loud, angry voices drifting down the stairs from the kitchen.

"Peter, you must convince your wife that she cannot have this baby! It is not the right time in your life to be having a child. You're still in school and you can't support a baby, and I am certainly not going to feed another mouth. I can't afford it, and I will not *tolerate* it. Now, you go downstairs and make her understand. *Do you hear?*"

She couldn't hear Peter's reply, but within minutes he was standing in the doorway, framed by the pieces of broken bamboo slats, looking frazzled. He sat beside his wife on the bed and gently stroked her hair, then leaned down and kissed the back of her neck.

"Honey, why are you doing this to yourself . . . to us? We promised father we wouldn't have children while I was in school. For God's sake, you're only sixteen. Kathy, look at me." He lifted her from the bed and cradled her in his arms. She offered no resistance. He rocked her like a child, and whispered in her ear, "Kathy, I love you. If you love me, you will stop this nonsense." She bolted from his arms, her bloodshot eyes burning. *"Nonsense?"* she shouted. "You call abortion nonsense? It's our *baby!*"

He reached for her again, but she pushed him away and glared. Peter's voice was pleading. "I know, Honey, I know. But it isn't as if we can never have another baby. We made a mistake, Kathy, and father is just trying to help us. Why are you so mad at him? It isn't his fault, it's ours. He's just trying to help." He reached again for his wife and pulled her close. She nestled her head on his shoulder and sobbed softly. "Please, Kathy, try to understand my father. We gave him our word of honor, something he does not take lightly. Don't you remember that?" Kathy nodded in silence. Peter lifted her chin and stared into her eyes. "I love you, Kathy. I will always love you. But you mustn't fight father on this. In the end, he will always win, and we will always lose. He knows what's best for us. We are very lucky. My father is a *chosen man.* He was born with an exceptional brain. We are ordinary people but being a part of his life makes us special. As long as we listen to him, learn from him, and obey him, he will always take care of us."

Kathy listened. She, too, knew Oskar was different. It was one of the things that had drawn her to him from the first time they met. She couldn't deny that she was awed by his intelligence, flattered when he would spend hours talking to her, always making her feel very important. Peter wiped the tears from her cheeks. "If you love me, Kathy, you will let my father do what he has to do."

"I need time to think, Peter," she replied, not looking at him. "Right now, all I want to do is go to sleep. I need time to think."

When he left the room, Kathy took off her shoes and slipped under the covers, her head spinning. She hugged her pillow and thought of the baby she was trying to save. Sleep came within minutes.

She knew she was being watched, even in her sleep. She opened her eyes to see Oskar sitting in the chair, staring.

"Kathy, my dear, we have to talk," he said, his voice barely above a whisper. "Could you come into the kitchen for a while? Hanna has made us some coffee, or would you prefer tea?"

"I... I don't—"

"Yes, you do. It will make you feel better. Come, I will help you." He reached for her arm, but she pulled it away, swung her feet to the floor, and followed him to the kitchen.

Hanna reached into the cupboard for two cups and placed them on the table. Kathy watched her, wondering what the older woman was thinking. Why had she been so silent? Surely, she could understand Kathy's feelings, being a mother herself. How could she be—or pretend to be—so removed from this turmoil? Kathy tried to make eye contact, hoping for a sign of support, but Hanna poured the coffee and left the kitchen without so much as a glance at her.

This time, Oskar sounded sympathetic. "I certainly appreciate your feelings, Kathy, but I think there are some things you do not understand. How could you?" He smiled and lifted her chin so she would meet his eyes. "You are but a child yourself. You don't want Peter to hate you, do you?"

Kathy eyebrows rose. "Hate me? What do you mean? Why would Peter hate me?"

"Well, he may not hate you right away, but when he realizes the responsibility of raising a child, and the burden you are placing on him at a time when his mind should be on his school work—what do you think this will do to your relationship? How do you think this is going to make him feel? And who do you think he is going to blame?"

Kathy closed her eyes. She hadn't thought of that. *Would he really hate me? Could he hate our baby? No, he wouldn't, I just know he wouldn't.* Stubbornly, she clung to her dream.

Hours later, exhausted, Kathy sat slumped in her chair. Oskar's arguments had been monotonous. She knew she was being bullied; still, she couldn't escape his logic.

"Think about it, Kathy," he said. "I am sure you will come to the right decision. I know you are a very smart girl."

47

She couldn't wait to be excused. All she wanted to do was put her head back on that pillow and sleep.

Her rest was brief. Peter was sent to wake her up. "How do you feel, Honey?" He stroked her hair lightly.

Annoyed, Kathy rolled over, blinked her eyes open, thinking: *What a stupid question—how does he think I feel?* She responded flatly, "Totally drained."

"Well, you can sleep later. My father wants to know if you have come to a decision."

"Peter, please. I'm too tired to make a decision today. For God's sake, stop badgering me! Can't you give me some time?"

"Time is what we don't have. You know we can't have this baby, so why are you torturing yourself?"

"I can't understand you, Peter." She sat up in bed, glowering at her husband. "If you help me, we can have this baby."

Peter shrugged. "I'm sorry, I can't," he said and left the room.

She stared after him, wondering what had made him such an ardent follower of Oskar. The word "robot "came to her from science fiction books she used to read before she was married, but she quickly dismissed it. An obedient son, whose European ways she, an American, didn't fully understand, probably was more like it.

The next morning, Kathy came into the kitchen where Hanna sat alone, drinking coffee. Her stiff posture cried silently, *Traitor! Promise-breaker!*

"Hanna, "Kathy began, "surely you must understand how I feel? Can't you talk to Oskar—"

She heard footsteps. Hanna heard them, too, picked up her cup, and scurried from the kitchen.

"Good morning, my dear, "Oskar said cheerfully. "How was your sleep? Good, I hope." He tweaked her nose.

Kathy pulled her head away. "I'm bone-weary. I couldn't rest, Oskar—my mind is full of confusion."

"What's to be confused about? The answer is very simple. I can help you, Kathy, if you will just be a little cooperative."

He filled his cup, pulled up a chair, and put his arm protectively around her shoulders. "You know there is only one solution to this

48

problem. You are a child pregnant with a child. You must know that makes no sense."

"But Oskar, I—"

"No, Kathy. Peter can't afford to buy milk for this baby, and you know it. Who do you think is going to pay for it? Me? I don't have the money. I'm saving money to buy my mother a plane ticket to come to America. Do you want to deprive me of seeing my mother before she dies? How can you be so selfish, so ungrateful?" She could see rage welling up in him. His was barely controlling his voice.

Kathy was frightened. It was obvious Oskar's patience was wearing thin. Her gut feeling warned her that she was on thin ice. She knew she was fighting a losing battle.

"Where's Peter?" she cried. "I want to talk to my husband."

"What do you want him for" Oskar snapped. "This is your decision, not his. Anyway, he's already told me he does not want a baby." Oskar grabbed her hand.

"Let go!" she shouted, wrenching it free, then turned and marched from the room.

He began to get up to follow her, then sat down again. She was like a tidal wave stomping toward the door; then she was gone. "You have until lunchtime tomorrow to make up your mind," he called after her. "We can't wait much longer."

Downstairs, Kathy fumed as she dressed. How could he be so unfair to her and why wasn't Peter there to defend her? Where was he, anyway? Damn it!

She waited all day for his return, but by nightfall, she knew Oskar's will was being done.

CHAPTER 6

1960

Daylight! Kathy rolled over, reaching for her husband. She sat up in bed, panic rising in her throat. In the mirror above her dresser she saw herself, her eyes hollow and dark. *Where's Peter? Why are they keeping him from me?* The house was ominously silent. She bounded up the stairs in a hurry, looking down the hallway and into the kitchen. She looked out the door. The sun blinded her. Where could he be? She felt cut off from the family she had grown to love, in the house where they shared so many happy moments. The newfound haven seemed to be slipping through her fingers. She wanted things to go back to the way they were. *Am I the one who is wrong?* The strain of isolation was beginning to take its toll.

She went back to the Bamboo Room and cried herself to sleep.

She opened her eyes to her husband's angry face. He sounded anxious. "Kathy . . . Kathy, wake up. My father wants your answer, Kathy. He says we can't wait any longer."

She started to protest but stopped. His eyes were empty. Her heart began to thunder as she listened to his deadly cold words.

"If you insist on having this baby, you will have to have it alone. You will have to leave this house."

There was a long silence between them. Leave, without Peter? Where would she go? Home? *This* is her home, the only *real* home she had ever known. Besides, she hadn't spoken to her mother in months. She knew she'd find no sympathy there. She remembered her mother's reaction when her sister Joan came home with an unwanted baby. Alice had called her "pussy" and "scum of the earth" and chased her out of the house. And what of Peter? She couldn't think of life without him. She would rather die than lose him. Tears fell silently on her cheek.

Suddenly, she heard Oskar's loud voice as he trounced down the stairs. "I have had enough! Who does this American bitch think she is? If she can't do the right thing, get her out of my house!"

Kathy cringed at Oskar's wrath. She saw him standing before her in a rage. "Just look at what you've done to this family. You're a very bad girl. You have absolutely no appreciation for all we've done for you. Why can't you wait? You and Peter have plenty of time!" Her head seemed to explode, like a hundred tiny firecrackers bursting at the same time. The only words she heard were *you and Peter, you and Peter.* Could that be possible again? Could she get it all back again? Had she not completely destroyed the only sanctuary she had ever known? Anything, she decided in that instant—I'll do anything.

Sensing the change, Oskar lowered his voice. "I promise you, Kathy, everything will be all right. You know I always keep my promise." Like a tiger on the scent of its prey, he growled. "Hanna. . . boil up the instrument!"

Peter watched his mother, waiting for her to finish her work. Oskar had decided that, for legal reasons, he did not want them in the house while he performed the abortion and suggested that they take a very long walk.

It was still light out when Hanna and Peter left. The house was so silent Kathy heard the key click in the door. Her heart began to race wildly as she heard Oskar's footsteps in the hall.

"Katherine, my dear," he said politely as he reentered the room, "it is time for you to go into the bathroom. I have drawn a bath for you, and I want you to sit in the hot water and relax for a while. I will be with you shortly."

Kathy obeyed. The bathroom was small, and the hot water steamed up the window. A large white towel had been draped over the closed toilet seat next to the tub. With icy, trembling fingers, she removed her clothes and threw them in the wicker hamper in the corner. She stepped out of her sandals onto the cool tile floor and dipped her hand into the water to test the temperature. Catching a glimpse of herself in the mirror, she turned sideways, rubbing her stomach, wondering what she would look like if she were farther along. What difference did it make? It was too late now. She reluctantly stepped into the tub and slid as far down as she could, letting the hot water cover her shivering body. She closed her eyes, and a tear escaped.

The hair around her neck curled up in tiny, wet ringlets. The water licked beads of perspiration from her face. Kathy wondered what her mother would have to say about all this and vowed to never tell.

Oskar entered the bathroom. "Don't be afraid," he whispered soothingly. "Everything will be all right. Just relax. You are in good hands."

Kathy's blood rushed to her face as she realized that Oskar was staring at her nude body, a wide smile on his face. She wanted to hide her head under the water. Instead, she lay motionless, frozen with fear, and closed her eyes. She smelled smoke, and knew Oskar was sitting on the toilet seat, smoking, watching and waiting. Suddenly, she felt him touch her nipples, tweaking them, as he sometimes affectionately did her nose. Her eyes shot open and she bolted upright in the water, the sudden movement causing it to spill on the floor. She wrapped her arms around her chest. Oskar howled with laughter, his eyes twinkling.

"Relax, Katherine, I won't hurt you." He stood up, dropped the large white towel to the floor, lifted the toilet seat, and discarded his cigarette butt. Hiking his pants up at the knees, he knelt beside the tub on the towel, playfully splashing water into her face. "Lie back, my dear, I want you to relax." He unfolded her arms and placed them by her sides. She didn't resist. "I must relax your body completely before I can begin my work."

He started to massage her neck, talking in a monotone, his hands lightly touching her breasts. Feeling her stiffen, he whispered, "No, Katherine, you must relax. . . relax . . . loosen your body. Please, Katherine dear, do as I tell you. You must not fight me."

He splashed the water in the tub, playing like a child. "C'mon, Katherine, enjoy it." Suddenly, a twisted smile appeared on his face. His hands began exploring her body; his fingers walked down her stomach, lightly poking at her navel, finally resting on her thighs. "Spread your legs, Katherine." He pushed them apart. "You must allow the water to enter your body. It must be cleansed. It will be much easier if you cooperate."

Again, her body stiffened as his fingers entered her. But his massage was gentle. "Doesn't that feel good?" She could feel the heat from his breath on her face as he leaned closer to her. He kissed the top of her head. "I will not hurt you, Katherine. Just relax." Abruptly, he stood up, his voice now deep and husky. He picked up the towel from the floor

52

and handed it to her. "Here, dry yourself and go to the bedroom. Relax on the bed for a moment, and I will be right in."

Like an obedient child, Kathy stepped out of the tub, pulled the towel closely around herself and walked down the hall.

She stopped in the doorway, stunned. *Oh no,* she thought, *not the feather bed!* She had dreamed so often, from that first day with Peter, of sleeping in that bed with him. Never had she imagined that she would be lying on it before her father-in-law, who was about to abort her baby. Her eyes again filled with tears. She was still in the doorway when Oskar appeared.

"Why are you standing there? I told you to lie on the bed and relax! Look, you're still dripping. Here, let me help you." Oskar sat on the edge of the bed, his legs spread open, and pulled Kathy toward him. He gently patted her dry. When he spoke again, his voice was solemn. "Katherine, this is very important. Please listen carefully and do just as I say." He made her lie on the bed and sat next to her. She stared at him, her eyes wide in anticipation. "Abortions are never pleasant, but I can make it easier for you." He rested his hand on her stomach, stroking it ever so lightly. "I will be as gentle as I can. But first, in order to do this properly, I must get you to reach a climax."

Kathy's throat was tight with fear. Somewhere in the distance she heard him continue, "You know, after intercourse the womb opens to allow the sperm to pass through, so that the egg may be fertilized. Since the instrument I invented must follow the same path, it would be much better for your womb to be receptive. Therefore, it would be much better, and easier for me, if you had a climax before this procedure. "Kathy began to shake again, more from fear than from the cold. She watched in disbelief as Oskar stood up and began to unbutton his pants. "Since Peter is not here," he continued, "I will have to help you with that myself."

Kathy tried to scream out, but the words would not come. She shook her head back and forth, but fear prevented her from speaking.

"You know how much I long for you, Katherine." His pants were on the floor.

She wanted to bolt from the bed and run as far from the house as she could. But her legs did not move. Her eyes were fixed on Oskar, who had begun to lubricate himself with Vaseline. His penis, now fully

53

exposed, was already engorged; his flushed face bobbed over his thick neck, veins popping out. She was revolted.

He smiled down at her as he began to fondle her. "Are you getting in the mood?" He panted.

She stared at him in disbelief. How could a man who thought he knew so much ask such a stupid question? "No! No!" she moaned, struggling like a trapped animal trying to free herself. But Oskar quickly mounted her.

Kathy's throat filled with bile. She remembered cowering, as a young child, in the corner of the kitchen. Her brothers and sisters were running and screaming, because Alice was chasing them with the wooden spoon. Or maybe Alice was chasing them with the spoon because they were running and screaming. In that house, it was never easy to tell. Kathy hid, hoping to become invisible. *Maybe no one will see me,* she had thought as she hugged her knees tightly to her chest, *and they'll go away.* She wished that now.

She felt Oskar's hands raking her body, but she lay paralyzed. He took her arms and pinned them over her head, his hot breath smothering her face. She heard him laughing as his thrusts grew stronger. Her back began to hurt and she squirmed. He took it for pleasure.

"That's my baby," he whispered in a hoarse voice. "Just relax and enjoy it."

It seemed to Kathy like an eternity. He continued to whisper in her ear. "Are you getting ready, Katherine? I can't wait much longer." She wanted to scream: *Just get it over with, damn it!*

Suddenly, he cried, "Katherine, please love me, I need you so much." Finally, it was over." When his body fell limp, he burrowed his head deep into her neck and began to cry. The weight of his body covered her like a wet blanket as he held her prisoner in his arms.

At last, he stirred. He sat at the edge of the bed, his elbows resting on his knees, and began puffing on a cigarette. His words were slow and thoughtful. "You know, Peter must know about us."

Us? Kathy thought. *He must be kidding. Does he really think I liked it?* She dared not show her emotions. Would this never end? Now that she was resigned to the inevitable, she just wanted to get it over with.

"Do you want to tell him, or should I?" Oskar continued.

Tell him what? she wanted to scream. *Are you going to try to get Peter to believe there was more to it on my side?* She lay, shaking her head, tears streaming down her cheeks, but said nothing.

Oskar looked at her with affection. "Perhaps we should talk about this later." He reached for the instrument that Hanna had left at the bedside in a pan of water. "It's time for work. No more fun and games." Kathy felt cold and sticky. And, deep inside, her secret fastness was no longer whole. She knew it had been torn open, ripped apart. Oskar came at her again. She could feel him spreading her legs wide. With a careful thrust, he plunged the instrument deep into her body. She felt a fierce, sharp pain and screamed out. Oskar's hand came down hard over her mouth. *"Shut up!"* he hissed. "Do you want Oma to hear?" Suddenly, the world spun round and round and went dark.

The sound of her own scream awakened her. Her body ached. She felt the sheet beneath her already congealed with blood. Turning her head, she saw Peter asleep, his arms tightly wound around her waist. She moaned, recalling the pain and humiliation of the past day. Peter opened his eyes and leaned to kiss her. He gently brushed her hair from her forehead and cheeks.

"Honey, are you all right? I've been so worried about you. Last night you were delirious. I didn't know what to do."

She couldn't look at him, not after what had happened. She turned her face away, tears cascading.

"Don't cry. It's all over now." He used the corner of the sheet to dry her tears. "Shhh, everything is going to be all right now. You'll see, everything is going to be just fine."

"Peter, you don't understand. It can never be all right again. Not after what happened."

"Oh, *sure* it will, honey. Wait and see. In a couple of weeks, you'll forget all about it."

"I'll never forget it," she cried. *"Never!"*

Peter cradled her in his arms and rocked her like a child. "Peter?" she whispered; her head tucked deep into his chest.

"Um?"

"Do you know. . . I mean, did your father tell you what he did to me yesterday?"

"Yes, he told me. Please Kathy try not to think about it anymore. You'll just drive yourself crazy. What my father did, he had to do. Don't you understand that?"

"No, don't!" she shouted. "Did he tell you he had sex with me before the abortion?"

She felt him stiffen and realized that he hadn't known. He held her for a moment then, releasing her said, "I'm sure father had a good reason."

"My God, Peter, do you understand what I just told you? Your father raped me!"

Peter was silent. Slowly, he rolled out of bed and reached for his clothes. She could see his hands trembling. He left the room without a shirt or shoes. The bamboo strips rustled wildly in his wake; his footsteps pounded the stairs.

Within minutes, she heard Oskar's voice and knew they were quarreling. She rolled over and hid her head under the pillow. She was sure Peter would be on her side.

He returned hours later. Kathy had been dozing on and off. Now, as he stood before her, his face expressionless, her fears returned. There was a hangdog look in his brown eyes. She listened, stunned, as he tried to explain that he believed his father's side of the story: there had been no trespassing on Oskar's part. "If . . . if you didn't have some feelings for my father, you wouldn't have let him do it. And, as long as there are feelings on both sides—uh, then, in that case, it's all right."

"All right?" she screamed. "Peter, you must be *kidding*. How can you agree to let any man, never mind your father, have sex with your wife? You don't really believe him, do you?" She started to cry.

"You never tried to stop him, did you?"

"Peter!" She was pleading with him now. "He told me that in order for him to perform the abortion, I had to . . . to reach a climax first. He said that, since you weren't there, he would have to do it himself. I swear, I was so scared, I didn't know what to do. I . . . I didn't have a . . . a climax, but I didn't tell him, because I didn't want him to do it again."

She could see by the lack of expression on his face that she was not getting through. "I don't care what you believe," she screamed at the top of her lungs, "I don't ever want him to come near me again. I hate him, I hate him, I *hate him*!"

* * *

"You've got to eat, Kathy," Peter said as he sat beside her on the bed, holding a plate of potato pancakes smothered with applesauce. "You haven't eaten in two days. You can't stay in this room forever, you know."

She looked at him with disgust. "I'm not hungry."

"Ah, c'mon, Kathy, I know you love potato pancakes. I had Mother make them special, just for you. Please . . . just a little?"

Peter had been very patient with her over the last few days, trying to convince her that everything was fine. He repeatedly assured her of his love and promised that someday they would have at least two children.

Now, he put the fork to her mouth. Slowly, she began to eat. She hadn't realized how hungry she was.

Pete nodded. "That's my girl. We'll get you back on your feet in no time. Kathy, there is something I must explain to you about my father. I've had many long talks with him in the last few days and I believe him when he tells me that he loves you deeply. Of course, he loves us both, but he has a special need for you. In time you will learn to understand him and his ways." He smiled at his wife and continued trying to make her understand.

"I can understand his love for you, Kathy, because I love you, too. When you love someone, sex is a natural feeling, a way of communicating, a giving and sharing. Oskar says sex *is* love! Please try to understand him, Kathy. He has great needs and he really can't help himself. Things will be so much easier for you—for both of us—if you go along with his wishes." He lifted her chin and kissed her lightly. "Remember Kathy, when you make him happy, you make me happy."

He leaned over to kiss her, but she moved away crying, "Peter, I can't believe you really want me to do this. I just can't believe you."

"You must, Kathy. Right now, you're the only one who can help him. Perhaps," he got up from the bed, went to the dresser, opened the top drawer, and handed her a sheaf of papers, "perhaps, if you read this, maybe you'll be able to understand him better."

She recognized Oskar's handwriting and angrily threw the papers to the floor.

Peter picked them up, sheet by sheet, and laid them on the nightstand. "When you're feeling better," he said quietly, "read them. If you love me and want us to have a life together, you'll understand."

Kathy burst into tears. "Oh, Peter, I don't know what to do! I only know I love you and want us to be happy together. I'll try, Peter, I'll really try."

The next morning, when Peter left for school, Kathy picked up Oskar's essay titled 'Sex, A Means of Communications.' She was startled when she heard his voice; she didn't hear him enter the room. "Katherine, my dear," his voice friendly, cajoling, "I am happy to see you looking so well. But you must get some air. You can't stay in this room forever. I have brought you some freshly brewed coffee." He placed the cup on the table next to her bed. An expression of feigned surprise appeared on his face. "Well, what do you have here?" He reached across and pulled papers from her hand. "Where did you get these?"

"Peter gave them to me. He wants me to read them," she explained, biting off her words. "He thought it might help me to understand you a little better."

"Smart boy, that son of mine," Oskar said, still pretending he had nothing to do with getting the essay into Kathy's hands. "But what is so difficult about me? Am I so hard to understand?"

"Yes, at. . . at times."

He appeared not to be listening as he scanned the pages. "Have you read this?"

"Yes, I have."

"And what do you think?"

"Well, I don't understand a lot of it."

"I didn't expect you would, Katherine. How old are you now, sixteen? What would a sixteen-year-old know of life and its complications? That is why I keep telling you that you need me . . . to teach you, to guide you, and to help you understand. But still you resist me. Believe me, I can do much for you, if only you will listen to me. Why

58

don't we make peace and try again? You have so much to learn, and I have so much to give." He placed his hand on her shoulder. "Why don't you be a good girl and get dressed? We will take a walk in the sunshine. I'm sure you will feel much better. I'll explain my essay to you." He leaned down and gently kissed the top of her head. "I'll wait for you outside." He turned and left the room.

Kathy thought about what Peter had said. Her self-imposed exile had given her much time to think. She pensively sipped her coffee. Was she ungrateful? Where would she be if it hadn't been for Oskar? Hadn't he helped her when she needed him? She and Peter would not be married if it hadn't been for him. She wouldn't be living in this nice, quiet house. Again, she recalled Peter's words as he kissed her good-bye that morning before he left for school: "He has a special need for you. Life will be much better for both of us if you keep him happy."

She finished her coffee and got out of bed. The terror had passed, like a dream from which one eventually awakens. She felt alive again. The thought that Oskar really needed her took on a new meaning. It made her feel important. She believed it would also make Peter grateful to her, perhaps make him love her even more. Her face flushed with excitement, Kathy quickly dressed and walked into the morning sunlight.

Oskar was waiting. She greeted him with a smile.

"What a beautiful day," she said. "I feel better already."

"Yes, my dear," Oskar responded as he reached for her hand. "Every day is beautiful if you make it so."

* * *

Later that evening, she wrote Oskar a letter:

Your visit this morning was very nice. I'm sorry I was not in a very good mood. It's taken me a long time to understand what happened. It really gives me a good feeling to know you are not mad at me. I know you are not an ogre, or anything like that. Thinking about the things you said to me afterwards made me feel guilty, ungrateful for all the things you have done for

59

me and Peter. I mean it felt so good to know you really didn't think badly of me. I know you really wanted to help. I'm sorry. I didn't understand. I must get over my silliness and know I can talk and confide in you. Before talking to you, I had quite an uneasy feeling. I do not want to do that, especially over one misunderstanding. I MADE A MISTAKE. I'M SORRY. I WON'T DO IT AGAIN. If possible, I would like very much to keep our good feelings. You showed me a very different side of you today— understanding my youthfulness and ignorance. Now, I want to show you and Peter a different side of me.

DO YOU FORGIVE ME?

CHAPTER 7

1960

By the Labor Day weekend, Oma returned to Germany.

One morning, shortly after Peter left for school, Kathy lingered in bed. The aroma of freshly brewed coffee told her Oskar was up and about, although she could not hear him move. It had been almost three months since the abortion, and Oskar had gone to great lengths to regain her confidence. Even his critiques of her writing had been considerably tempered. Whenever they were in a room together, she could feel his eyes on her. He would lightly brush her hand as they passed each other. More and more, he engaged her in conversation; they began to share laughs again.

The bamboo curtains rustled and, although Kathy did not turn, she knew it was Oskar. She smelled the coffee as he placed the cup on the night table. He lowered himself to the edge of the bed and began massaging the back of her neck.

"How's my baby today?" he asked. Playfully, he pulled the covers from her. "It's a beautiful day, Katherine. How about sitting in the yard with me?"

She rolled over, stretching languidly. Through the opening in her gown, Oskar's hand began caressing her breasts. Kathy sat up quickly and reached for the coffee.

"How do you feel today, Katherine?"

"I don't know." She said, her voice full of sarcasm, "How *do* I feel?"

Oskar howled with laughter. "That's one of the things I like about you, Katherine. You're the only one around here with any sense of humor." Slowly exposing her breasts, he asked, "Did Peter ever tell you how beautiful they are? Kathy felt her face flush, but she offered no resistance. She had learned it was easier to accept his advances and avoid his fury. The abortion had almost torn her loose from her moorings and drowned her in his rage. She would not risk that again. She watched as Oskar lowered his head and nuzzled her breasts, kissing them lightly. Then he stood up.

"Well, shall we walk in the yard?"

"I'd like to take a quick shower Oskar. I'll be right with you." She jumped from the bed and reached for her robe, pleased that he had asked no more. She took the stairs two by two and headed for the bathroom.

She turned on the warm water and stepped into the tub, closing the drain, her heart still racing. The water soothed her nerves, and she leaned back and closed her eyes. They flew open when she felt his touch. Oskar stood before her, naked. Neither spoke. He stepped into the tub and whispered, "You don't mind if I join you, do you, dear? I promise you won't regret it."

Kathy didn't respond. She closed her eyes and turned her back to him. Waiting…

"Americans know very little about the real pleasures of life, "Oskar continued. "They lack the control, which gives the ultimate pleasure. Control, my dear Katherine, control and discipline are the key words. Only the Germans know their true meaning."

Kathy was no longer listening to him. As though in a trance, she felt him kissing, probing her till she screamed for him to stop. He stopped, kissed her lips lightly, and whispered, "Control, my dear. You must practice control." He stepped out of the tub, rubbed himself dry, and held out a large towel for her. She only wished it were Peter.

Thereafter, it became a way of life for her. She no longer complained to Peter. Oskar was her master and she was his slave.

The things he said and did shocked her less and less now. Somehow, he would make them seem reasonable, normal, acceptable. Sometimes she wondered if she were going to hell, but always Oskar would think of some new way to explain that life as he preached it was healthy, the way nature intended, that bodies were beautiful and meant to be used to the fullest. Since her intimate relationship with Oskar was now family knowledge, everyone started to speak freely and openly in front of her. She became one of them. Now that she had accepted Oskar's ways, they no longer quarreled, although she still feared his anger. She felt she had matured a great deal in the past two years, and had learned how to placate Oskar, especially since discovering the pill. When she first suggested it, Oskar was apprehensive; he never trusted anything or anyone but himself. After thoroughly researching the subject, however, he allowed

62

her to use it, but not without a resounding admonition: "If you take the pill, you must be disciplined. Remember—take one a day without fail." Kathy promised and promised and promised.

* * *

The rain pelted against the kitchen window as Kathy piled leftovers on the table. Cleaning out the refrigerator was not one of her favorite chores, but Oskar had complained the night before of stale odors coming from it, so she had promised to tackle it first thing in the morning. It was a depressing job, and even though the music from the radio blared loudly, her spirits were low.

It's probably the weather, she thought, *or maybe I'm just plain tired. Between Oskar and Peter, I'm exhausted.*

She had tried to think about other things, but nothing seemed to lift her spirits. She had spoken to Ingrid, who, despite her father's objections, had run off and married her boyfriend, Erik. Now Erik was in the hospital, gravely ill.

Kathy was restless and bored. Peter was in the middle of exams and had little time for her; she hadn't spoken to her mother in months and was beginning to feel guilty; and Hanna, oh hell, Hanna was hopeless. In the beginning, Kathy had tried to befriend her mother-in-law, but with her relationship with Oskar so open now, she had given up.

Kathy took all morning to clean the refrigerator. It was after noon when she walked into the basement workshop. Oskar, as so engrossed in his work, he didn't hear her. She watched for a moment as his hands steadily worked with minute electronic components. She admired his dexterity.

When Oskar finally became aware of her presence, his face lit up.

"What a nice surprise," he said, greeting her with a kiss on the cheek. "It's about time you came looking for me."

"I'm bored, Oskar," she said quickly. "May I take a bus and go downtown for a while?" Her question went unanswered.

"Come in, my dear, and look at what I've done this morning." He gingerly picked up a complex device. "Isn't it beautiful?"

63

There was a long silence as Kathy pretended to examine a jumble of odd-shaped little boxes. She had no idea what it was. She beamed back at him. "Everything you do is wonderful, Oskar."

"I'm so glad you've finally come to appreciate my talents, dear Katherine. Come." He patted his knee. "Sit on my lap and tell me your problem."

"It's not really a problem . . . it's just that I'm bored today. I have nothing to do this afternoon. I've cleaned out the refrigerator, and I thought that maybe, just this once, I could go downtown for a little while."

"To do what? It's raining out."

"I know. Maybe I could go to a movie or something."

"That's a great idea. How about looking at some home movies? Would you like to see some pictures of my old girlfriends?" Not waiting for an answer, Oskar pushed Kathy from his lap and stood up. She could see he was excited.

"Come, I'll set the projector up in your room, and we can relax on your bed and watch the films." He put his arm around her waist.

He aimed the projector at the white wall at the foot of the bed. The first frame was a shot of an attractive young woman with very long, dark hair sitting on a bed, dramatically stretching her legs high into the air as she removed her black fishnet stockings.

"That is Carola," Oskar explained. "She and I were lovers in Germany. Isn't she lovely?"

The woman stood up, slowly unbuttoning her dress, letting it drop at her feet. Her body, though well proportioned, was full. She bent over, showing the camera a very provocative angle of her behind as her long hair rolled luxuriously over her shoulders to the floor. With a dramatic sweep of her hand, she pulled her hair from her face and held it high in the air, smiling at the photographer.

Oskar was enjoying the show. "Aren't these films great? I took them myself many years ago."

Kathy didn't respond. Her eyes were fixed on the screen. The woman reached her arms behind her back, released her bra, and flung it over her head. Her large breasts fell dramatically lower. Just as she began to wiggle her way out of her panties, the film began to flicker to a halt.

Oskar jumped from the bed, bellowing, "Goddamn it, just when it starts getting good, the film breaks."

When he fixed the break and turned the light off again, Kathy saw Carola lying nude on the bed, her legs spread wide. Oskar pulled Kathy closer, his arousal beginning to rise. The woman rubbed the palms of her hands over her breasts, causing her nipples to stand erect. The smile on her face broadened as her hands stole to her inner thighs.

Oskar's breath was hot on Kathy's neck. "Carola is begging me for money so that she can come to America to visit me," he whispered, "so you'd better be good to me, my pet."

Kathy turned to him. "You still write to her?"

"Certainly. We're still friends. But don't worry, Katherine, I told her I can't afford to send for her right now. Peter's school is costing too much money, and I can't afford another expense at this time. Maybe later. Why, are you jealous?" Oskar chuckled.

"What does Hanna have to say about that?"

"Hanna? Hanna has nothing to say about it. I am the boss in this house. Anyway, she has known Carola for a long time. When we were in Germany, we all lived together for a while." The film continued to roll as Oskar reminisced about their time together. Suddenly he called to Kathy, "Look, my pet, look how Carola misses me." The woman was masturbating. Oskar reached for Kathy, his breath hot, his penis erect.

"Oh, no, you don't," Kathy teased, struggling to free herself from his grip. "I'm not going to let you take your hots out on me, not when she's warmed you up."

Oskar held her tighter. "You are a bitch, just like Carola, only you are a spirited one. I like that." He pulled her down on the bed and whispered, "Do not worry, my pet, I still love you more than anyone else. Do you love me more than you love Peter?"

Kathy's heart began to pound. She had carefully avoided answering this question many times before for fear that the truth would draw his wrath. She decided, as always, that a kiss would be a suitable replacement for an answer.

"That's my girl," Oskar said with a note of pride in his voice. "It has taken me a long time to train you, but it has been worth it. You are no longer an American brat!"

A single beam of light from the forgotten projector spot-lit the bedroom wall, and their laughter drowned out its humming.

CHAPTER 8

1961

Ingrid's calls came in rapid succession as her husband's condition deteriorated. Bone cancer, she had told Kathy. Kathy had been appalled to hear they had amputated Erik's leg, but it was supposed to save his life. Now Ingrid was on the phone, crying that the doctors had been wrong. Erik was dying.

Kathy had grown very fond of Ingrid and cried with her when she heard the news. She begged Oskar to let her go to Missouri to be by Ingrid's side, but he refused.

"I need you more than she does," he insisted. "Besides, I cannot afford the fare."

"I'm so sorry," she told Ingrid on the phone. "I wish I could be there with you. I begged Oskar to let me come, but he won't listen to me. Please don't cry, Ingrid. Hold on, and I'll get him for you."

She dropped the receiver and ran to the stairs, shouting, "Oskar, come quick! Ingrid's on the phone, Erik is dying!"

Oskar's expression never changed as he picked up the phone and listened to his distraught daughter. Kathy stayed close to his side so that she could hear. "Father, I'm so scared," Ingrid was saying. "I don't know what to do. He is critical."

"Well, the sensible thing to do is to get out the insurance policy and make sure it's paid up."

"Oh God, Father, how can you think of such a thing?" Ingrid cried.

"Because when your husband is dying, that's the first thing to do. Check the insurance policy. Certainly, you're not surprised, are you?"

"Yes, I am. When they amputated his leg, Dr. Rosenbaum told me..."

"Dr. Rosenbaum? You believed a doctor with a name like Rosenbaum and now you're surprised? For years, I've told you of their inferior mentality—"

"*Please* don't start lecturing me now. I'm too upset to listen to you."

"Upset, upset," he repeated calmly. "What's to get upset about? You knew when you married Erik that he was a sick man."

"Yes, but I never thought he'd die, at least, not so soon. I just thought . . . oh, Father, I've had him such a short time . . ." Ingrid wept.

The indifference on Oskar's face troubled Kathy. As she glowered at him and turned to leave the room, she heard him say, "And don't forget, Ingrid, you still owe me two thousand dollars. When you collect the insurance money, you'll have no excuse not to pay me."

Kathy slammed the door and ran out to the backyard, fighting tears. She wandered aimlessly, her arms clutching her stomach roiling with anxiety. What would I do if it were Peter? She began to cry and realized almost immediately that her tears were not for Ingrid alone. For some time now, she had suspected that she was pregnant. The thought of Oskar's wrath, when he would find out, made her tremble with cold fear.

*　*　*

From the doorway, Peter saw his wife's head bent over a magazine. She was sitting under the large oak tree. He crossed the yard quietly and, leaning over the back of the canvas chair, kissed her cheek.

"Oh, Peter!" she cried. "You scared me."

"Who did you think it was, the boogie man?"

"No," she replied flatly. "I thought it was your father."

"Let's not start that again, Kathy." He sat on the grass; the smile gone from his face. A tone of reproach came into his voice. "What's wrong? Why are you avoiding him? You know he enjoys your company."

She slid from her chair and nestled beside him on the grass. She was crying.

"Please, honey, tell me what's wrong!"

She threw her arms around his neck, hugging him tightly. Her heart was pounding. She had tried to tell him before, but each time the words got stuck in her throat. She felt his arms around her, comforting her, and she summoned enough courage to quickly blurt out, "Peter, I'm going to have a baby!"

68

She felt his body stiffen, and he pushed her away. She tried to meet his eye, tears streaming down her cheeks. "Please Peter, don't tell Oskar, please. I don't want to have another abortion."

Pete finally looked at her, his eyes narrowing. "How is that possible, Kathy? You've been on the pill, haven't you?"

"Yes, but I forgot . . . once, Peter, just once. I didn't think one pill would make a difference."

"You didn't think it would make a difference? Oh, Kathy, how could you?" He shook his head. "How many periods have you missed?"

"Three."

"*Three?*" His mouth hung open. He jumped to his feet and stared at her. "Good God, Kathy, what is wrong with you? Doesn't your word mean anything to you? You promised my father . . . you assured him you were trustworthy. You promised him over and over that you would take the pill faithfully every day." His accusing finger was like a metronome. "Did you deliberately deceive him?"

"No, Peter, I swear. It was an accident. I didn't do it on purpose, I just forgot."

"How could you forget something so important, especially when you knew Father would have a fit?"

Kathy glared at her husband.

"When are you going to stop worrying about your father and start worrying about us? When is it going to be just you and me?"

"We made a promise, Kathy. We must keep our word. That's the way I was raised. My word is my honor. I guess you don't understand that." He turned his back to her and began to pace, his hands pushed deep into his pockets.

Kathy started after him. "I'm sorry, Peter, I didn't mean to do it. I swear it was an accident."

"Why did you wait so long to tell me?" he asked, softening his tone.

"Because I wanted to keep this baby. Please, Peter, can't I have my baby?"

He reached for his wife's hand. "Come, we must talk to Father."

Oskar was a madman. Kathy cowered at his rage. She sat in the kitchen and watched, her eyes filled with terror as he paced the floor, shaking his finger in her face as he berated her.

"You are an ungrateful child. You don't appreciate a damn thing I've ever done for you. You've taken advantage of my love and done nothing but wasted my time. You've used up all my money and haven't paid a damn bit of attention to all the things I've tried to teach you. You don't love me. You don't give a damn about me. All you care about is yourself. You're a selfish bitch. You're nothing but an ingrate!"

Peter, leaning against the kitchen door, stared at the floor, not knowing quite what to do with his hands, as his father continued to vent his anger.

Oskar turned and raised a fist to him. "And you. You're just as bad as your wife. You're nothing but a weakling, a coward, always were. A skinny, whining coward with not an ounce of backbone in your body! Didn't I tell you not to trust her? Didn't I tell you Americans can never be trusted? In spite of all I have tried to teach her, she is still an American bitch!"

Turning back, Oskar bent over her, his hands pressing on the arms of her chair, and shoved his face right into hers, staring into her eyes. "Honor thy father?" he said. "Do you know what that means? Of course you don't. How could you? You didn't even have a father! This is the thanks I get for trying to be a father to you!" he shouted. "Get out of my sight, both of you. I can't stand to look at you anymore."

Kathy welcomed the dismissal and jumped to her feet immediately, but Oskar grabbed her wrist and pushed her back into her chair. "Not so fast, young lady. I have one more thing to say to you!" His words were now slow and menacing. "Mark my words, there will be no baby! I will not allow it! Tomorrow morning, I will take you to Dr. Schultz. He'll fix you good!"

Kathy ran out of the room, shaking. Peter did not follow her. Instead, he went into the living room where his mother sat ignoring the ruckus in the kitchen.

Kathy did not know when or if Peter came to bed that evening; when she awoke in the morning, he was gone. Except for the pounding rain, the house was silent. She got out of bed and began to dress, her heart beating wildly. Forgetting the pill had truly been an accident, a mistake she wished she had never made.

Kathy did not make mistakes, not often. She told herself that she must follow Oskar's orders carefully. She had heard many tales of Dr. Schultz but had never met him. She knew that he and Oskar were old friends from Germany.

Suddenly, Oskar was there. Lips pursed, he snapped, "You're dressed. Good. Let's go."

She caught a glimpse of Hanna in the kitchen as they went down the hallway, pretending to be oblivious of the happenings. Kathy silently followed Oskar to the old jalopy waiting for them at the curbside. She looked for Peter. He was nowhere in sight.

They drove in silence, the ride all too short. They stopped in front of a large, run-down house, rang the doorbell, and waited. Oskar impatiently rang the bell a second time before a wild-haired man in his early seventies opened the door. The sight of him unnerved Kathy. His back was badly bent, and he wore a monocle in his left eye. When he held open the door, she noticed his twisted, arthritic fingers. She looked beyond the door into a musty, dark hallway leading to a small, cluttered room. The examining table in the middle of the room revealed years of neglect. The doctor greeted them politely with a heavy German accent.

"Remove your clothes and get on the table." It was more of a command than a request.

"All of them?" she asked meekly. Leaning against the doorjamb, Oskar chuckled. "Since when are you bashful? Just take off your clothes and shut your mouth." He turned to the doctor, smiling. "These damned Americans . . . they talk a lot but say little." The doctor joined Oskar in laughter, as they shared a private joke.

Kathy draped her clothes over a nearby chair and climbed onto the table. The cold leather made her break out in goose bumps. The doctor leaned over her and began to examine her breasts. Kathy turned her face away from the stench of his sour breath.

The examination was cursory. The doctor turned to Oskar and said with authority, "It is too late, much too late for an abortion." He shook his head vigorously and added, "Much too dangerous. Come," Dr. Schultz took Oskar's arm, "let us go into the other room. We must have a little talk."

Moments later she heard Oskar shout, "Get dressed, Katherine. Wait for me outside."

*　*　*

For the next four days, Kathy was given pills four times a day with little water and no food, except soup, tea, and coffee. She was forced to remain on her feet, not allowed to sleep for any length of time. Oskar continued to berate her. She cried constantly. Peter refused to interfere, and Hanna, as usual, saw nothing and did nothing. Only once did Peter weaken. He asked his father to let Kathy sleep just for a little while.

But Oskar erupted into another fit of rage. "Mind your own business! I'm doing what I have to do." He paused, and his eyes seemed to flicker, momentarily softening. "Remember Peter…whatever I do, I do in your best interest."

On the fourth day, Kathy was so sick and exhausted that even the ache had gone out of her body. She had tried to reach her mother. She was slumped on the floor in the corner of the kitchen, trying to hide the phone, when Oskar entered the room.

"What the hell do you think you're doing? Give me that damn phone!" He yanked it from her hand. "Who the hell were you calling, your mommy?" he said viciously. "The next time I catch you trying to call her or anyone, I'll break your arm!" He grabbed her wrist and pulled her from the floor. "Get up, you bitch. I told you to keep walking. I've got to watch you every minute."

She struggled free of his grip and tried to run from the room. He grabbed her hair, spun her around, and slapped her hard across the mouth with the back of his hand. Blood spurted from her mouth and trickled down her chin. The force of the blow knocked her back to the floor. "Please, Oskar, don't hit me," she begged. "I feel so sick." She dropped her head to her knees. Her arms felt like lead weights; she could barely lift them. Suddenly she heard anxious footsteps in the hallway. Peter rushed in, tripping over a chair. He picked her up and cradled her in his arms.

"Please, Oskar, may I take her to our room? Can't you see how sick she is?" He looked up at his father, his voice trembling.

Oskar nodded. "It's only a matter of time now."

Peter lifted Kathy into his arms and carried her down the steps. She was sweaty and trembling. He laid her down gently and covered her with a blanket, tucking her in. Then time stopped for her.

When Kathy opened her eyes, she had no idea what time or what day it was. She touched a hand to her swollen lip and winced. She tried to sit up, but the pain in her back forced her down. As her awareness came into focus, she looked around the room for Peter. He was in the chair next to the bed sound asleep. She moved to reach him and realized that she was lying in a pool of blood.

"Peter!" she screamed. Too weak to rise she fell back on the pillow.

Peter jumped from the chair.

"Please, Peter, take me to the hospital or I'll bleed to death," she pleaded.

"I can't, Kathy, not yet. Oskar says it's too early." He reached for a washcloth that was lying in the basin next to the bed and began to bathe her face with tepid water. "It's almost over, honey."

"Oh God, Peter," she moaned, "how much longer do I have to wait?"

"Soon. He says it'll be real soon."

"Help me up, Peter, I have to go to the bathroom. I can't just lie here in this mess."

"Okay, honey. Here, put your arm around my neck and lean on me." She was almost on her feet when she suddenly cried out, "Momma! Help me, Momma! I think I'm going to die!" Her body fell limp.

Frightened, Peter put her back into the bed and ran upstairs, calling for his father.

Kathy faded in and out of consciousness. Oskar and Hanna stood over her, and Pete begged his father to call the doctor. Oskar refused. Instead, he told Hanna to clean up the mess.

The next morning, Kathy felt her husband shaking her, felt him wrap her arm around his neck and pull her from the bed. She struggled to open her eyes and heard him say, "Kathy? Kathy, can you stand? Please try. Oskar wants to see you upstairs." The room spun round and round as she tried to focus her eyes, bile rushing to her throat. Her body was wracked with pain, her legs felt like jelly, and she clung to Peter as they climbed the stairs.

Oskar was waiting in the kitchen, relaxing in his captain's chair, his legs spread apart, a large white pan between them. Chips of enamel had broken away from the edges, exposing the iron underneath.

"Well, well, so the princess is awake," he said. There was no mirth in his voice. "Come here and squat over this pan. I want to see how much you are bleeding."

"No," she whimpered. "No, please."

"Do as you are told," he commanded as he yanked her away from Peter.

She tried to hold onto her husband. "Please, Peter. Don't let him humiliate me like this. Don't make me do this!"

"Kathy, Kathy," Peter coaxed, a cold sweat on his cheeks, his eyes stealing timid glances at his father, "you're only making it harder on yourself. Do as he says."

Oskar pushed the pan toward her. "Stop moaning and squat. I haven't got all night."

With one last hopeful glance at her husband, Kathy lifted her robe and obeyed.

Oskar frowned as he watched the blood splatter into the pan. "Take her back to your room, Peter. She's still not ready."

Kathy's piercing screams filled the room. She did not stop screaming until her body went limp and she felt as if she were no longer a part of it. She could hear herself crying, feel her husband carrying her, but was powerless to move. She wondered if she had died.

Sometime during the night, Peter tiptoed up the stairs into the kitchen. He dialed the phone, whispered his name and address, "Please hurry, I must take my wife to the hospital. She is very, very sick. And sir, please don't honk the horn when you arrive. I don't want to wake anybody up."

CHAPTER 9

1961

"Please wait over there," a woman behind the admitting desk told Oskar. She pointed to a dull-beige alcove furnished with a set of wooden hospital chairs. "You must first see the doctor about your daughter-in-law. He'll be here in a little while."

"I don't want a doctor," Oskar fumed, "I want my daughter-in-law. Have her brought to me. Now!"

The receptionist remained unruffled, impenetrable. "You will have to wait for the doctor, sir," she said, adjusting her reading glasses on her nose and returning to her paperwork. Oskar had no choice but to comply.

"American bitch," he muttered, sitting stiffly on one of the chairs, his fingers drumming impatiently on his knees.

It was almost a quarter of an hour before a dark-haired, white-coated young man came into the waiting area and addressed him.

"Good morning, sir. My name is Dr. Roth. I understand you're looking for me."

"I'm not looking for you, I'm looking for my daughter-in-law, Katherine Kunz. I've come to take her home."

"I'm sorry, sir, but your daughter-in-law is in no condition to be released from the hospital. She's lost a tremendous amount of blood and is in a very weakened state. She needs a few days of bed rest."

"She can get all the rest she needs at home, doctor. My wife will look after her. I can't afford to pay the hospital bill."

"I don't think you understand, Mr. Kunz. Your daughter-in-law is a very sick young woman. She was in bad shape when she arrived here last night. She had already lost the fetus and was bleeding profusely. We've done everything possible to stop the bleeding, but she should be watched closely. I must insist that she stay here for at least another day. It is crucial that she remain under our care."

"If she needs any further medical attention, I will take her to a qualified doctor," Oskar sneered, "one who graduated from the University of Berlin. Now, if you don't mind, *Dr. Roth*, I've no more time to waste here. Please sign the release or whatever is necessary to relieve yourself from this case and let us go."

The doctor hesitated. Finally, he said, "I want you to understand that I'll sign a release only on your representation that Mrs. Kunz will be seen by your own physician."

Oskar nodded.

"Also, I would like you to ask him to call me so that I can discuss her problems with him."

Oskar nodded again, impatiently.

"I'll tell him, doctor, but it won't be necessary for him to consult you. He already knows her problems."

Dr. Roth seemed about to protest again, but apparently decided that any further efforts would be futile. He turned to the woman behind the desk, spoke to her in a low but crisp tone, and left. Oskar waited, stewing, while the woman typed and handed him the release.

* * *

After her return from the hospital, Kathy was isolated in the Bamboo Room. Oskar and Hanna did not speak to her, did not call her to meals, acted indeed as if she were, once again, an invisible child. And Peter, like a whipped dog, crept to her side just briefly enough to bring her food and to slip into their bed at night. As a result, she turned more and more to her diary, to pour out her anger, her fantasies, her loneliness—and something else, a stirring within her, a growing resolve to take control of her own life and live it to suit herself, not Oskar. For now, she could write whatever she pleased, and she was determined to show Oskar none of what she wrote. Let Peter and Hanna submit their writings to him; she wouldn't. She couldn't—for it would reveal what she was only just beginning to admit to herself: her growing hatred of the man who had nearly killed her.

From among the broken sentences and doodles, these words stood out in large letters:

MUST GET AWAY. . . MUST GET AWAY . . . MUST GET PETER AWAY FROM OSKAR . . . MAYBE I COULD GET HIM TO RUN AWAY AND GET A JOB!

And then she wrote one word repeatedly across the page, in bigger and bigger block letters, followed by exclamation marks:

YES! YES! YES!!!!!!

The weeks turned into months. Peter would not budge, and it forced Kathy deeper into depression. She sat on the edge of her bed staring at the notebook resting on her lap. The open pages were covered with words in broken clumps. Words that reflected her churning, disturbing thoughts, the deepest still remained unwritten. She no longer believed in Oskar's way; she could no longer fit into his world. She had learned it the hard way. She had finally grown up. She had finally found her own voice. She had had enough. She had tried it Oskar's way, but it was too painful.

But Kathy's determination to keep her distance disturbed Oskar. He knew she was deliberately avoiding him, so he presented Peter with a complaint. The two stood in the hallway. Oskar fiddled with a piece of circuitry as he spoke with a maligned look on his face.

"You must talk to your wife, Peter. I never know where she is anymore. She gets up early, leaves the house without telling me, and I don't see her again until late afternoon. It's dangerous for her to be wandering around the streets. You never know who she is going to talk to, or what she might say. I have told her repeatedly that what goes on in this house must stay in this house, but I don't trust her anymore. You must get her under control. After all, I can't do everything for you: she's still your wife."

Peter, who had listened to Oskar's lament motionlessly, eyes averted, replied defensively, "All right, I'll speak to her again."

That evening, Peter and Kathy argued. "Where do you go?" he wanted to know. "Oskar says you're gone all day long."

"I don't go anywhere special. I just don't want to be near him. And I certainly don't go up to strangers and tell them your father abuses me.

77

The only thing I do is. . . sometimes I call Momma, but I would never tell her anything."

Peter pressed her. "Where do you spend your time?" "Sometimes I take King for a walk, and sometimes I sit at the bus stop and wait for you. Is there anything wrong with that?"

"No, except Oskar knows you're deliberately avoiding him." Peter's voice was shrill, vexed. "Why must you always create problems?"

Kathy screamed back, "Me, create problems? Jesus Christ, Peter, you've got it backwards. What about him? Did it ever occur to you that he's the one who's creating the problems?"

Peter grew angrier. "I can't do anything about him," he said in a clipped voice that was meant to sound tough, "but I can do something about you. You're my wife, and I want you to stop causing trouble in this house." He turned his back to her and walked away.

That night Peter did not kiss her good night. Kathy cried herself to sleep but kept her determination.

Days passed and still Peter wouldn't speak to Kathy. They ate dinner in silence and then he would retreat to Oskar's workshop and stay there until he knew she was asleep. In the morning, he left quietly for school, without saying good-bye.

The isolation from Peter became so painful she finally began questioning herself. *What have I done? Have I lost Peter?* Her questions remained unanswered, but of one thing she was sure. She loved her husband and did not want to live without him. She picked up her pen and wrote:

I don't like myself at all. If he seems strange, perhaps it's because of the way I've been treating him. I always seem to see the sour things in life. How can I be so empty and lackadaisical? How can I expect him to love this type of person or even show any interest in me when I won't do the things he wants me to do? Why don't I act ladylike? Even elegantly, the way I really want to? No, instead, I'm Miss Gloom and Doom. What I need is patience and more energy. I must keep this picture vividly in my mind. If I think of a person I would want to love or idolize, it is generally a picture of a happy, energetic, kind man. Energy in reserve for necessities- working energy- the kind that shows through every day. How can I expect any less from him? How can I expect this type of person to show any interest in me? Why? Why, when people show feelings for me, am I awkward—like a fool I shirk it off! I will try to act happy! No . . . I WILL BE HAPPY!!!!

Kathy's determination grew with every stroke of the pen. By the time Peter came home from school that evening, she was convinced that it was she who owed him and his father an apology.

By evening's end, she lay in Peter's arms, her face wet with happy tears. She had not only apologized to Peter but had begged Oskar's forgiveness, too, and things in the Kunz household slowly returned to their ugly normality.

CHAPTER 10

1963

In the fall of that year, Ingrid's husband died. The young widow was thinking of coming back east to live with her parents. Kathy wished she would. Oskar forbade her to associate with anyone outside the Kunz household, and she was in dire need of a friend.

But Christmas passed, and it was spring before the arrangements for Ingrid's return were made. On the eve of her arrival, over supper, Oskar was reminiscing about the good old times before "that fool of an Erik" took away his lovely daughter. He held forth now his hope for the life the family would lead now that it was made whole again. The family lingered at the supper table late into the night as Oskar drank more than usual, flushed with the excitement of his daughter's return.

In the early morning hours, something woke Kathy up. She opened her eyes and saw the bamboo strips swaying before she felt a light touch on her arm. She jumped, startled. Oskar loomed over her in the dark, his finger pressed to his lips.

"Shhhh," he whispered, "Don't wake Peter."

"What's wrong?" Kathy asked, raising herself on her elbow.

"Nothing. I can't sleep. I'm too excited about Ingrid coming home. Come, come to my room so that we can talk."

"Oskar, I'm tired. We'll wake Hanna . . ."

"No, we won't. Hanna is sleeping in the living room. I've already sent her there. Come!"

Kathy looked at the clock, threw herself back on the pillow, and moaned, "Oskar, it's three o'clock in the morning!"

But Oskar would not be denied. He seized the covers and flung them, grabbed her feet, and dragged her off the bed. Kathy groaned loudly enough that Peter rolled over on his side and, seeing his father in the room, rolled back pulling the covers over his head.

Dazed and shivering, Kathy felt herself being nudged up the stairs. She stopped for a moment to look into the living room. Oskar had not lied. Hanna, indeed, was sleeping there. He took Kathy's arm and led her into the master bedroom.

When Kathy awoke late that morning, she found herself still in the feather bed. She sat up and looked around, expecting to find Oskar in the room. He wasn't there. She went exploring and found the house empty. They must have gone to meet Ingrid, she thought. At first, she felt left out, she had wanted to be among the first to welcome Ingrid back. But, she decided, it had been considerate of them to let her sleep, knowing that Oskar had kept her up all night. The thought of their kindness made her feel better.

After a leisurely shower, she got dressed and went into the kitchen to make coffee. The coffee was already made; five cups sat out on the counter. A delicious smell wafted from the oven. Kathy glanced at the clock, surprised to see it was past noon.

She heard laughter and saw Ingrid striding through the door, the rest of the family trailing behind her. The bustle reminded Kathy of all the welcoming warmth she felt in this house as a young bride, so very long ago. She hurried down the hallway, into Ingrid's arms. Delighted to see her, Ingrid smiled, but Kathy thought she looked pale and drawn. Peter pushed past them, carrying his sister's luggage.

"Come, come," Oskar called, "it is time to open the wine and celebrate. My little girl has come home!" They crowded into the kitchen, pulling the clunky chairs around the table already set with starched white linens and the best family china, a bowl of fresh daffodils at its center.

"Oh Momma," Ingrid said, "it's been so long since I've had a good home-cooked meal. It smells so good!"

"It's been a long time since I've had a good home-cooked meal, too," Oskar said with a sheepish grin. He lightly swatted Hanna across the back side as she tasted the sauerbraten. She smiled at his attention.

They talked and drank beer while Hanna, her cheeks unusually pink with joy, served dinner. She had, indeed, outdone herself. As Oskar asked for seconds—which pleased Hanna tremendously, Kathy wondered just what kind of a spell Oskar had over his wife. She never questioned any of his decisions, responded instantly to his demands, and always seemed to be on alert, waiting for something. But for what?

A shiver ran down Kathy's spine.

"Are you cold?" she heard Peter ask.

Before she could answer, Oskar responded, "Cold? Who can be cold on such a lovely day?" He looked at Kathy. "Go help Hanna with the dishes, that'll warm you up. And while you're up, get me another beer."

As the women cleared table, Oskar began to speak. Table talk was a ritual, and Oskar was always the reigning king holding court. Now, though Oskar was still undeniably the master of the house, in Kathy's eyes he no longer seemed regal to her. "It has been such a long time since the whole family was together. We have much to talk about." Oskar began, "Tell me, how much insurance did Erik have?"

"Twenty thousand dollars." Ingrid responded.

Oskar's eyebrows danced, and he let out a slow whistle. "Twenty thousand dollars. Not bad, not bad. Well, I'm glad the poor bastard was good for something."

"Oh Father," Ingrid groaned, "how can you say that? I thought you liked him."

"I did, I did, but he was never good enough for you." Oskar guffawed as he picked up his beer bottle and took a long swig. "Then again, sweetheart, most fathers never think the men their daughters marry are good enough for them, yes? By the way, what are you going to do with all that money?"

"I haven't decided yet, except I plan to use some of it for a vacation. I need a break."

Oskar thought otherwise. He gave Ingrid a litany of his outstanding bills and segued into a long dissertation on the family's need for a new furnace. Then he expounded on the obligations of children to reimburse their parents for at least part of the costs of their upbringing.

Finally, Ingrid stood up and stretched. "I'm exhausted. I'm going to bed. We can talk more about this tomorrow."

* * *

The sun was bright and warm when Kathy walked out into the backyard the next morning. Ingrid sat alone under the oak tree, drinking coffee. "Where's Oskar this morning?" Kathy asked.

"He had to go into the city early, so he left with Mother. Come sit with me. They probably won't give us too many chances to talk alone, so let's catch up. What have you been up to?"

Kathy sat on the grass and rested her head against the tree, happy at last to have someone to talk to. "Nothing exciting. I'd rather talk about you. What are you going to do now that Erik is gone?"

"I don't know." Ingrid began to cry. "I honestly don't know what to do." It seemed that Ingrid needed a friend as badly as Kathy did. For the next hour, the young widow talked about the long, frantic nights in the hospital at Erik's side and the torment of knowing there was no hope. "I have no definite plans. The only thing I do know is that I need a nice, long getaway."

This sounded like the miracle Kathy had been praying for. Maybe Ingrid could help her get herself and Peter away from Oskar? Peter would graduate in June. Perhaps, just perhaps, they could all go on a trip together?

"Kathy, are you listening to me?" Ingrid asked. "You seem to be a million miles away."

Kathy reached for Ingrid's hand, but before she could speak, Ingrid asked,

"What's wrong Kathy, are you and Peter having problems?"

"No, no, not me and Peter. It's Oskar. He's— He's—" Kathy hesitated, wanting to tell, yet uncertain how Oskar's own daughter would take her accusations. She tried to evade the subject. "It's just that . . . that I think it's time for Peter and me to get a place of our own. Would you . . . Ingrid, could you just maybe suggest to Peter that we all take a vacation *together*? If I could get him away from Oskar for a little while, I might be able to convince him that it's time for us to get our own place when he's done with school. Oskar doesn't want us to move out because he says he can't run the business alone."

"He probably can't," Ingrid agreed. "He never did like to work. He'd prefer to have Peter work at the business while he plays with his stamp collection or his Dresden figurines. But yes, I think you and Peter ought to have a place of your own."

"Will you help us then? Will you talk to Peter?"

"Sure, I think it would be great for us all to go on vacation together. I would love it. Between the two of us, the poor guy won't stand a chance." Ingrid beamed at her sister-in-law.

"It's good to have you back home, Ingrid. Sometimes it's so lonely around here."

"Is that why you look so sad?"

Kathy closed her eyes for a second. When she looked up, tears flowed down her cheeks.

"There's more, isn't there?" Kathy nodded. "Do you want to tell me about it?"

"I . . . I don't know whether I should, but I can't keep it to myself anymore. I just need to talk to someone." As tears rolled down her cheeks, Kathy brought Ingrid up to date on everything that had befallen her since her wedding day. Ingrid listened in silence; her eyes filled with empathy.

Feeling more and more certain that she could trust Ingrid, Kathy confided that she occasionally called her mother but had never told Alice—or anyone else—about her abortion and miscarriage.

"When Momma asks me if I'm happy, I tell her half-truths. What I want to tell her is that I am still very much in love with Peter, but that I am miserable living here, because of Oskar." Kathy hadn't intended to tell Ingrid about Oskar, but it seemed that once she started to speak, she couldn't stop. The words and the pain just poured out of her. But fear overcame her again; fear that she had made a grave mistake in confiding in Oskar's daughter. She peered anxiously at Ingrid's face. It was stony but showed no signs of incredulity or shock. When Ingrid finally spoke, her voice was soft.

"I'm so sorry, Kathy. Really sorry for what my father has done to you. I'm not going to make excuses for him, because I can't. I know only too well what he's like. You see..." Ingrid hesitated, before continuing, "I went through it too, a long, long time ago!"

"You? You and . . .?"

"Yes, Father and me. My father is a sick man, Kathy. We've all known that for a long time. My mother has been putting up with it for years. I don't know how she does it. She's not dumb, but she's strange. She can just pretend nothing is happening. I think she still dreams that someday he'll change, that he will just give up his ways and be the husband she has always wanted. But it won't happen. Father thinks the whole world is mad and he's the only sane one in it. He thinks he knows everything! If you don't believe it, just ask him. I learned a very long time ago that he simply sucks the life out of everyone around him until he gets his way."

Kathy listened thirstily, soaking in the calm reassurance that she was not the crazy one.

Ingrid continued, "Did Peter ever tell you what my father did to me?"

"No."

"When Erik and I first began dating, we were seventeen. Father kept asking me if we were sleeping together. I told him no because it was the truth at the time. He called me a liar, then said, 'You tell me you love each other and then you expect me to believe you're not sleeping together? What is he, a queer or something?' When I told him there was nothing queer about Erik, he said, 'Well, then, is there something wrong with *you?*' I tried to explain that we weren't ready for a commitment, but he just didn't understand. He yelled at me, 'What the hell does commitment have to do with love? When you decide to marry, you make a commitment. When you're in love, you have sex. It's as simple as that.' And then he said, 'Just because a man gets married doesn't mean he can't sleep with other women. That's just another stupid American affectation.' How many times have you heard that one, Kathy? A hundred times, I'm sure."

"At least."

"Finally, I did sleep with Erik and I came home and told Father. I wanted him to know that Erik wasn't queer, and that I was also a normal girl. I should never have told him." Ingrid lowered her head and began to pluck at the blades of grass, searching for the right words. Finally, she cleared her throat and said, "Since I was no longer a virgin, Father felt he had a duty as a father to teach me . . . to show me the proper way to have sex. He wouldn't leave me alone. Every day he badgered me to sleep with him. Sometimes he'd say he just wanted to be sure I knew what I was doing. That didn't work, so he started to play on my feelings as his daughter. He never used physical force," she added hastily, almost defensively, "but he used all the power he had over me as a father. He used reasoning and logic. He said that if the ancient Egyptians could do it, why couldn't we? Then he begged and pleaded with me, and finally cried. He cried real tears, Kathy, and I just couldn't take it. Can you believe a big bully like him crying?" Kathy looked at her sister-in-law and wanted to yell, *Sure I do! He used those same tears on me!* But she said nothing, because now Ingrid was crying. "After . . . after weeks of this, I gave in. I just couldn't stand it anymore. He would say things like, 'Would you deny water to a man dying of thirst?' In the end, he made me believe it was my duty as his daughter to give him what he wanted. He convinced me that I owed it to him. Like the furnace—you know?"

"I know exactly what you mean," Kathy said bitterly.

The noon sun had become hot and bright, and Ingrid put her hand up to shield her eyes. Her fair skin had begun to redden. She rolled over on her stomach, propping herself up on her elbows. When she spoke again, her voice was more controlled.

"When I told Erik about this, I thought he was going to kill my father. I can still see the anger on his face. It's too bad, Kathy, that you never got to know Erik. You would have really liked him. He was different from any other guy I knew. He's nothing like my father! I guess that's why I fell in love with him. He was really wonderful."

"What did Erik do?" Kathy wanted to know.

"What could we do? He's my father! So, Erik insisted that we elope. And that's just what we did."

"That's what Peter and I need to do. I mean, it's too late to elope. We've just got to get away, Ingrid, I can't take it here anymore."

From the house came a muffled sound of the radio. The young women looked at each other, abruptly silenced. Oskar had returned from the city.

*   *   *

Peter was easily won over to the idea of taking a vacation with his sister and his wife. He was bored with school, excited about graduating and leaving, and tired of the work his father was heaping upon him. Still, it was taking him a while to summon up the nerve to broach the subject with Oskar.

86

Kathy and Ingrid started to get impatient. Late one spring evening, Oskar and Peter came up from working together in the basement workshop, and the family gathered in the kitchen for a beer before going to bed.

"Father," said Ingrid pointedly, "Peter wants to tell you about the plans we're making. Go on, Peter."

"We want to take a vacation," Peter said. He sounded apprehensive. "Ingrid is going to buy a car with some of her insurance money and take us someplace."

"Nonsense! Nonsense!" Oskar shouted. "You're better off here! I need you here, all of you. What do you mean you want to buy a car? What business have you buying a car, Ingrid? We need a new furnace. I told you that. The old one is stinking up the house. It's filthy, it's unhealthy, and you talk of buying a car. Why do I have to pay all the bills around here? You've got twenty thousand dollars. My own daughter has twenty thousand dollars in insurance money and doesn't even give me a dime! Now that's gratitude!"

Peter looked at Ingrid, a clear expression on his face. *What did I tell you?*

"That's not true," Ingrid responded angrily. "I've given you money, Father, and you know it. Peter needs a vacation. He's been working for you fourteen hours a day, he really has. Can't you see he's under a lot of pressure?"

"Pressure? What do you know about pressure?" Oskar's voice was shrill with rage. "I'm under more pressure than all of you put together."

Peter began to withdraw, but Ingrid would not back down.

"Kathy and Peter have never even had a honeymoon. Aren't they entitled to even a little break?"

There was no winning an argument with Oskar. This conversation was only a prelude to weeks of nonstop bickering, which culminated in Ingrid giving her father money for a new furnace.

Next, Oskar decided that he needed new machines for his business. His current ones, he said, were inadequate to handle the volume of business, which was sure to increase with the onset of Christmas season, only six months away. Ingrid gave in again and supplied six thousand dollars more for the machinery.

Two weeks later, as the family sat around the kitchen table, drinking their nightly beer, Ingrid announced that she bought a new car. Oskar exploded.

"Was it necessary to buy a *new* car? Wouldn't a used car suffice? You know how desperately I need a car for my business, for the running of this household, and you go and waste money on a fancy new car? Have you no consideration for your family? Aren't the needs of this family important to anyone but me?"

The color in Ingrid's face began to fade, the excitement replaced by resentment. When she could stand it no longer, she shouted back at her father, "What did you do with all the money I gave you? I gave you at least two thousand dollars more than you needed for the furnace and the machinery. What happened to that money?"

"Well," Oskar said defensively, "I bought some collector's items. I didn't do it for me. I really did it for all of us. They were a good price. They will appreciate in value."

"What?" Ingrid screamed. "You're yelling at me for buying a new car when you sit there and tell us you spent two thousand dollars on china figurines?!"

Furious, Ingrid pushed her chair away from the table and stormed out of the kitchen as the phone rang. She ignored it and kept going. The phone continued to ring until Peter got up to answer it.

"Hello?" He listened to the caller on the other end of the line.

"Who's calling?" As Peter listened for the reply, a look of astonishment came over his face. He put his hand over the mouthpiece and, staring incredulously at his father, he spoke almost in a whisper. "Somebody named Janice Williams wants to talk to you. She says she's your daughter."

Oskar jumped up. A broad grin on his face replaced the anger of moments before. Without a word of explanation, he grabbed the phone.

"Janice? Janice, honey, is that you? What a pleasant surprise. Where are you calling from?"

Kathy glanced at Hanna, whose face was frozen.

Oskar's voice, loud and exuberant, took her attention away from Hanna. She looked up as he hung up the phone. "Hanna, can you believe it? That was Janice. She wants to come and visit me." Hanna did not respond. Oskar turned to her again. "Isn't that wonderful?"

It was Peter who responded and asked: "Who is Janice? Why did she say she was your daughter?"

"Because she is!" Oskar bellowed proudly. "Janice is my daughter." He went on to explain, in unnecessary detail, that Janice was conceived in Germany by his then-mistress Else, who had married an American and was now living in California.

"But," Oskar bragged, "Janice wants to see me. After all, I am her father!" He further explained that he and Else had stayed in touch, that the seventeen-year-old Janice began to clash with her stepfather, and that Else suggested she might want to go live with her father.

Oskar turned again to his wife. "Hanna, isn't that wonderful?"

"Yes, Oskar. Wonderful." Hanna attempted an unsuccessful smile. Apparently, she had been aware of this relationship for some time.

Peter was still stunned. "Why didn't anyone tell me?"

"What for?" asked Oskar reasonably. "What does it matter to you?" He turned back to Hanna. "We must make a room ready for her."

Kathy had had enough. She was disappointed that this total stranger had interrupted her great plan for escape. She rose from her chair and left the room.

She went to Ingrid's room and found the door locked. Disappointed, Kathy retreated to the Bamboo Room. It was hot and airless. She undressed, slipping into a thin nightgown, one of Peter's favorites, and glanced in the mirror to reassure herself that she looked pretty.

While she waited for Peter to come to bed, she picked up her notepad:

Something new every day, not one but two new sisters. What do I care? We're going on a vacation in Ingrid's new car. I can't believe it, but this time we're going. Going ... going ... gone. Colorado, here we come! And we're NOT coming back to where we started from.

CHAPTER 11

1964

"Look!" Kathy shouted, turning to look at Ingrid stretched out in the backseat. "There's the first car with a Colorado license plate!"

"And there's the Colorado state line," said Peter, excited. "Did you ever think we'd make it this far?"

"No! I never did," Kathy exclaimed, kissing Peter's cheek. "Let's pull over at the next lookout so we can stretch our legs and look at the scenery. It's breathtaking."

"It certainly is," Peter said, "in more ways than one. I can hardly breathe."

"It's the altitude," Ingrid observed. "But you'll get used to it."

"Oh, Peter, I'm so happy! In a million years I never dreamed I would see Colorado." Kathy reached over and kissed him again. "I love you, honey. I hope we can stay here forever."

"Would you two cut it out?" Ingrid grumbled. "I'm hungry. Let's look for someplace to eat."

Peter pulled to a stop at a campsite in Rocky Mountain National Park, and they walked to the lookout. Peter held Kathy's hand; her face lit up with anticipation. Kathy took a deep breath of the crisp, fragrant air. She ran ahead of them, throwing her arms wide, twirling round and round till she sank to the ground. "We made it! *We made it!*" she shouted. "I can't believe it!"

Peter smiled at Ingrid. "It's good to see her so happy. This was a great idea, sis. Thanks."

"Peter," Kathy shouted, "do you know I've never seen a mountain before? My whole life has been spent looking at skyscrapers and dingy alleys." He started to say something, but she stilled him with another lingering kiss. "You had to boil the ocean to get me to cross the Brooklyn Bridge, and now there's no stopping me! I've never felt so alive in my life!"

Ingrid chuckled. "Kathy, I don't think I've ever seen you so bubbly!"

"It's because I just died and went to heaven," Kathy replied earnestly. "And if this is a dream, don't you dare wake me up."

They left the lookout and headed for the nearby diner. "I need coffee," Kathy cried, "real coffee, not that rotten instant we've been drinking all week!"

Peter grinned and let her lead their little party inside. Her happiness was infectious.

* * *

For the next two weeks, they drove in the mountains, crossing and re-crossing the Great Divide, sometimes heading southwest in rich farmland where sleek black cattle grazed, other times finding rushing crystal streams; now marveling at the black canyon of the Gunnison, now dipping into New Mexico, where they drove at sunset along a road that was itself like a narrow canyon gouged from rose-red rocks.

As they headed back toward Denver, the idea of moving to Colorado for good had started to take form.

They had tired of putting up and taking down the tent. Since they had heard of camps where, for a small fee, they could stake their tent, use the communal facilities, and enjoy the social life, they began looking for such a place. They found one a few miles outside of Denver. Peter stopped the car and gazed down into a beautiful valley, where a sea of tents surrounded a large wooden building. It looked like a haven, Kathy thought, guarded by the snowcapped peaks that soared above the valley.

The camp seemed to have everything. The owner's son, a bright twelve-year-old, showed them around. There were shower stalls, toilets, washing machines, vending machines, and a social room where movies were shown. And there was mail service, with some limitations. A large sign read:

NOT RESPONSIBLE FOR MAIL NOT PICKED UP ON DELIVERY DAY

Who cares, Kathy thought. *Any mail we'd get would only be bad news anyway.*

"Look," Peter said. "There's a pay phone. I think we'd better call Father. I'm sure he expected to hear from us before now."

91

Kathy panicked. She had been so happy she had almost forgotten he existed. "Don't call, Peter, please. You know you'll be asking for trouble."

He turned his tanned face to her, a face grown fuller and infinitely less tense. "I want to *avoid* trouble, honey, that's why I think we should call."

Ingrid agreed and handed Peter a handful of change. As he dropped the money into the phone, a shiver ran down Kathy's spine. She pressed close to him, wanting to hear the conversation, knowing what Oskar's first question would be.

"I really don't know when we're coming home," Peter replied. "It's so incredibly beautiful here, we thought we would stay awhile longer."

"You've been gone three weeks." Oskar's voice was loud. "Don't you think that's long enough?"

"We thought..."

"How can I get in touch with you if I need to reach you?"

Kathy turned and started to walk away when she heard Peter furnishing their address. "We won't be..." He didn't finish; Oskar had hung up. That evening, Peter lay still in her arms, his head on her breast. She held him tight and placed a gentle kiss on the top of his head. The happiness she felt just hours before was no longer there.

"Peter," she whispered, trying to reawaken it, "wouldn't you love to live here forever? I've never seen such beautiful country in my whole life."

"Yes, it is beautiful."

"Why don't we look around for a plot of land? Maybe someday we could build a house here. Wouldn't that be wonderful?"

He smiled. "Hmmm . . ."

The next morning, over breakfast, Kathy again brought up the subject with Ingrid. "If we found a piece of property we liked, would you lend us the money for a down payment? I promise we'll pay you back, with interest!"

Ingrid agreed without hesitation. "Sounds like a good investment to me. And if you don't pay me back," she said happily, "I'll just keep the land, right?"

92

"Then it's a deal?" Kathy asked.

"It's a deal."

They spent the next few days driving around with a realtor, who showed them even more gorgeous views. One lot in particular interested Peter—he told the realtor he would think it over and let him know, but Kathy saw that Peter wanted it.

They drove to Colorado Springs for dinner that evening. The lights down in the valley flickered like thousands of fireflies against the blue dusk. The air was cool, but their spirits were high as they celebrated their future.

They returned to camp to find a letter from Oskar. Peter's smile faded as he read it aloud:

Dear children:

Your lack of consideration and concern for your father disturbs me deeply. Peter's lack of responsibility concerns me even more. The pressures of the business are too much for me, and the silence in the house is unbearable. Do you think you are the only ones who need to rest? What about me? What about my needs? Doesn't anybody care what happens to me?

Kathy listened silently; her stomach tightened in a knot. She waited, afraid, knowing what Peter was going to say.

Ingrid threw a quick glance from one to the other. "Well, what do we do now?"

"Didn't I tell you not to call?" Kathy was angry. "You shouldn't have given him our address!"

She recognized the look on Peter's face, had seen it many times before. "We have no choice. We have to go home."

"Why? Because your father snaps his fingers?"

"No, Kathy," Peter replied calmly. "*I'm* going back because he's right. I've been irresponsible. I should have told him how long I would be away. He relied on my help, and I've let him down."

Within minutes of getting back to camp, Kathy had seen the expression on her husband's face change from relaxed and happy to tense

93

and stressed out. How could a wonderful evening in Colorado be poisoned by a few words written by a man thousands of miles away, in New Jersey? "Oskar can be so selfish sometimes!" she cried.

Ingrid chuckled grimly. "Selfish *sometimes*? How about most of the time! He's a man with an iron will. He gets what he wants."

"Peter," Kathy sobbed. "What about the land?"

"As a matter of fact," Peter said, trying to smile, "I just made up my mind about the land. Tomorrow, before we go to the airport, we'll go back to the realtor and give him a down payment."

Kathy was afraid to believe him. "Do you mean it, Peter? Can we really buy it?"

"Would I lie?" he said, grinning bravely. "Someday, I'll build you a beautiful house on that hill."

That night, the rain came. Peter's plane was scheduled to leave the next evening; he had promised Kathy his absence would be short. The rain pelted the tent so hard she started to hope his flight would be canceled altogether. She crawled into Peter's arms. The more she was with him the more she hungered for him.

By morning, the rain slowed down to a disappointing drizzle, but still, as they drove to the realtor's office, she was confident that something new and wonderful was happening. Their first real possession! A hope—a dream—becoming a reality!

Ingrid was as excited about the land purchase as they were. She drove them to the airport as they snuggled in the backseat, everyone talking at once. The girls would get jobs and wait for Peter to return.

Peter, too, was in high spirits. "I promise I'll be back in two weeks!"

Kathy blew her husband a kiss as he boarded the plane. "Love you, Peter!" she shouted. "Hurry back! I'll be waiting!"

CHAPTER 12

1964

As the bamboo strips rustled behind her, Kathy dropped her suitcase to the floor, kicked off her shoes, and stared at the bed she had shared with Peter since their wedding day. It was still legless, an island in the middle of a barren, dimly lit corner of the basement. *Nothing has changed,* she thought—*nothing except me.* A shiver ran down her spine when she thought of Oskar and his 'needs.' She had been gone for only two months, but it was enough to make her realize she couldn't return to the routine of the Kunz household. She wondered who took care of Oskar's 'needs' while she was gone. Hanna, who else? How had she tolerated living with him all these years? It was a mystery to Kathy.

Hanna hadn't come to the airport because, Oskar said, "she was tired as usual." He kissed Kathy on both cheeks and simultaneously rubbed her backside. "The vacation must have done you some good." He beamed at her with anticipation. "You look rested."

Peter waited for his father to step aside before reaching for his wife and kissing her hard on the mouth, the hunger of the kiss belying his apparent calm. For a brief moment, they were alone in the crowd, but Oskar quickly interrupted their interlude. "Let's get out of here. There will be plenty of time for that later."

Kathy clung to Peter, leaning on him as they made their way through the airport. "I missed you so much," she said as she snuggled next to him in the car. She could sense Oskar's jealousy but chose to ignore it, for the moment at least. Being near Peter was enough.

Kathy heard footsteps. Peter was coming down the stairs with the rest of her luggage. When he entered, she was standing in front of the mirror, clad only in her bra and panties. "Put them in the corner, honey. I don't feel like unpacking right now."

Peter crossed the room, and she could see from the reflection in the mirror that he was watching her. She deliberately picked up her hairbrush and began fluffing her hair, which had grown considerably since he last saw her. She knew how much he loved long hair. She heard him whisper, "You're so beautiful."

Half-turning, her voice teasing and soft, she asked, "Did you miss me?"

"You know I did."

She unfastened her bra and let it drop to the floor, stepped out of her panties, and stood before him nude. He held his arms out to her and she slowly walked into his embrace. They held tight, sprinkling each other with soft, tiny, wet kisses, savoring the smell of their bodies. Peter spoke first. "I'm so glad you're home. I've missed you so much. I was afraid you wouldn't come back."

It seemed like an eternity since he had held her in his arms. She had never considered not returning to him.

Peter groaned and kissed her breasts. They fell down on the bed together. Cupping his face in her hands, she turned it upward, staring into his eyes, searching for something that would tell her why she had to return to Oskar's house. She had been so sure the trip to Colorado was the beginning of their freedom. She ran her fingertips over his face, tracing his cheeks tenderly, wanting to make love to him, but the gnawing feeling in her stomach wouldn't let her. She needed to talk. She needed to know what would have happened to their marriage if she hadn't returned.

"Peter, I did a lot of thinking while I was away."

He murmured, "Can't it wait?"

"No. I need some answers. Why didn't you come back to Colorado? Is your father more important to you than me?"

Peter stilled her with a long kiss. "Does this answer your question?"

"That's not fair, Peter," she replied. She was serious. "Why did you send me such a cold, impersonal letter?" Her voice cracked. "Couldn't you have at least called me? Maybe we could have talked about it? Did you think I wanted to build a house in Colorado and live in it alone?"

She saw the pained look in Peter's eyes, the frustration on his face. "Are you listening to me?"

"I heard you, Kathy, but . . . I've come to believe that our Colorado plans were a little premature. I'm not sorry we bought the property, but it's not time yet. We have to wait awhile longer. My father still needs me here to help build his business." He looked at her with pleading in his eyes. "I owe it to him, Kathy. After all, he's done so much for us—putting me through school, helping us get married—I feel obligated to pay him back. I had hoped you would be a little more understanding. I feel morally bound to give him a little more time."

"How *much* time, Peter? We've been married five years now, and I want a place of our own. I want children. Isn't that what you want, too?"

Peter nodded. "Of course it is, but we have to be patient, just for a little longer." He tried to bring her back into his arms, but she pulled away and got out of bed. "C'mon Kathy, it's your first night home, let's not fight."

Kathy's voice was calm, but she felt rage rising in her. "I don't want to fight *with* you, Peter. What I'm trying to do is fight *for* you. But nothing around here has *changed*! I don't want to live this way anymore! I feel like a caged animal. I want an apartment, *our* apartment."

"With what? We have no money." Kathy heard the tension in his voice. "How can we pay the rent?"

She stood before him naked, a look of determination on her face. "Tomorrow . . . I don't care what Oskar says, I'm going to look for a job." She waited for his reaction, but he said nothing. He stood up and began to undress. He took off his trousers and hung them neatly in the closet, then unbuttoned his shirt and flung it in the hamper. The tight feeling in her stomach got worse. She had gone and done it again: pushed away the only person in the world she truly loved.

When next she looked at her husband, he lay on the bed naked, staring at the ceiling. Her eyes filled with tears and she threw herself across his chest. "I'm sorry, Peter. I didn't mean to upset you. I've been looking forward so much to being alone with you tonight. I'm sorry." She leaned toward him to give him a chaste, pecking kiss, but he put his arms around her and held her close. When their lips parted, the anger was gone from his face. "We'll work it out, honey. Tomorrow, I'll talk to father. Try to be a little more patient with him. I promise we'll get our own place, soon."

"Honey, that's all I want."

"I know," he said, kissing the tip of her nose. "But Kathy, do me a favor, please? Don't fight with Father . . . you can get so much more out of him with honey than with vinegar. Humor him for a little while longer.

It'll make things so much easier." He looked into her eyes, full of love, lifted her chin, and whispered, "Let's make love, it's been so long."

* * *

The room was dark, but Kathy could see the silhouette of her sleeping husband. She recalled the letter he sent her while she waited for him out West: *Now that my head is clear, I realize that our decision to live in Colorado was immature and irrational. I will not be returning.* And she recalled the sick twinge those words had caused, the twinge of barely repressed terror, the sinking realization that Oskar had won again.

She leaned over, kissed Peter's lips, and smiled pleased he was happy with her decision to return. Life without him was unfathomable. She became lost in a dream that wouldn't die, and she touched him to reassure herself she was home with him again. She felt the warmth of his body and lightly kissed his chest, wistfully running her fingers through his hair. Although she was exhausted, she couldn't sleep.

She had the urge to go to the bathroom. Pulling the sheets over Peter's chest, she slipped out of bed and tiptoed up the stairs. She knew at once that she was not alone.

"I've waited long enough." Oskar's voice was but a whisper. "It's my turn now."

Kathy's options were clear. This time, she had a plan. It would be wise to distract Oskar, to lull him into complacency, or he would stop them and that would never do. She would make things happen her way, using love and patience. She felt a way opening, an escape for herself and the spineless young man without whom she had no desire to survive.

Slowly, Kathy reached for Oskar's hand.

CHAPTER 13

1969

"Hello, Momma," said Kathy, the telephone tucked tightly under her chin. "How have you been? Did you get my cards?"

"Yeah I got yer cards, but what's the matter, yer finger broken or sometin'?"

"No, why?"

"Well hell, it's been almost two months since I heard from ya."

Kathy sighed. Her mother would never change, always picking fights. But then again, how could she have raised all those kids if she hadn't been a fighter?

"Uh . . . I've had a few problems, Momma."

"Ya tellin' me. Yer problems started the day ya married—"

"Momma, please, don't start lecturing me now. I thought you'd be happy to know I've got myself a job."

"It's about time ya got off yer ass."

"I'm starting work on Monday at Arnold's," Kathy continued.

"Arnold's?"

"It's a department store in Hackensack. I'm going to be a switchboard operator. Isn't that great?"

"Yeah, that ain't bad."

"I'm really excited about it, Momma."

The phone was silent for a few moments. Kathy could hear her mother talking to someone; she was saying, "My kid's got a job. She thinks she's a big shot now 'cause she got herself a job. Took 'er long enough."

Kathy hung up and bit her lip. She should have known better. Her mother's disdain for her was old news, but she had to stay positive. Her plan to get away from Oskar was taking shape and if her mother wasn't going to be supportive of her, well, then she had to be her own cheerleader.

Monday morning Kathy woke up early. After her shower she dressed in a simple white blouse and pleated blue skirt. She looked at herself in the mirror and was happy with her choice. She didn't want to be late for work. When she arrived, she was taken to the switchboard ready for the challenge. It was after lunch when she looked up from the switchboard and saw her supervisor walking from desk to desk handing out envelopes. As he approached, she smiled.

"How are you doing, Kathy?"

"Very well, Mr. Tarulli."

He handed her an envelope. "How do you like your job?"

"So far so good. It's easier than I thought, and everyone has been so kind to me. I know it is going to be a great place to work and make new friends."

"A pretty girl like you should have no problems making friends." Kathy smiled, flattered by the compliment, and, with slightly trembling fingers, safely zipped her first paycheck into her purse, which she kept stowed under the switchboard.

The lights on the switchboard flickered. "Keep up the good work." Mr. Tarulli walked down the hall.

Kathy cleared the board, waited for her boss to go back to his office, then called her husband.

"You're a lucky man, Peter Kunz," she began. "I've got my first check, and guess who I'm taking out for dinner tonight?"

"Oh, honey, I can't. I've got too much work to do."

"You can work all night if you want, but between the hours of five thirty and eight thirty we're having dinner! At a restaurant! I won't take no for an answer."

He started to protest, but she interrupted him. "I haven't got time to argue with you, Peter, my board is lit up like a Christmas tree. I'll expect you to meet me in the lobby no later than five thirty."

"Father will have a fit!"

"So let him. He'll get over it. See you later. Bye."

At five o'clock, Kathy reached for her purse, stood up, and stretched. Sitting still for eight hours was the hardest part of her job, but she felt exhilarated. She had money in her pocket, which she had earned herself, and she loved her first real taste of independence.

Kathy's office was on the fourth floor of the Arnold Building. The elevators were small and crowded, and the wait was long. When she got to the lobby, she looked at her watch: it was exactly five thirty. Peter wasn't there. As she paced the lobby, she heard her boss calling, "Kathy, do you need a ride?"

"No, thanks, Mr. Tarulli. My husband's meeting me for dinner. He's a little late."

As darkness began to fall, Kathy could feel anxiety creep into her stomach. She buttoned her coat and leaned against the wall. Why was he late? Did Oskar stop him from going out to meet her? *He's like a steamroller,* she thought, *crushing everything in his path . . .*

She didn't hear the footsteps as Peter came up from behind and grabbed her.

"You scared me to death!" she squealed. "For a minute, I thought you weren't coming." She kissed him hard on the mouth. "Any problems?" she asked as she put her arm through his.

"A few. But let's not talk about that now. I'm starving."

* * *

"So, the boss says, 'A pretty girl like you should have no problem making friends,'" said Kathy as the waiter served them coffee. "I think he likes me." Her face glowed in the flickering candlelight.

"What's not to like?" Peter observed. "You're a beautiful woman."

"You're just saying that because I'm your wife."

He smiled. "You're probably right. Lucky me."

The cold wind coming off the Hudson made Kathy pull up her collar and wrap her coat tighter, but she felt warm inside and happy, happiest she had been since her Colorado vacation.

"Hang in there," Peter said on the bus ride home. "There's a light at the end of the tunnel."

As long as she had him, Kathy would wait forever.

Oskar met them in the hallway, bellowing "You said you'd be home by eight! It is now eight thirty! Whenever you're with her, you forget all your promises to me, all your obligations!"

Peter shifted his weight from one foot to the other. "It's still early, Father. We have plenty of time to work."

"It should have been done by now. I've told you a thousand times, you play *after* your work, not before."

101

Kathy listened. The pattern was all too familiar. There was no joy, however small, that Oskar would not deliberately poison. She felt the blood rush to her head and the pressure build behind her eyes. Against her better judgment, she screamed, "Jesus Christ, Oskar, you make me sick! Can't you ever get off his back?"

He turned to her with bulging, fiery eyes and spat, "Who asked for your two cents, you little bitch? Before you came here, we never had any problems. You're nothing but a troublemaker." He shook his finger violently in her face.

"When will you learn to keep your mouth shut?" he went on. Kathy took a few steps back. "You American bitches never know when to shut up. All you do is talk, talk, talk. If you don't like it here, get the hell out!"

"With pleasure!" She stormed out of the hallway, taking the steps two at a time.

Peter shouted after her, "Please Kathy, go to bed. I'll be there as soon as I can."

She was filled with rage, more at Peter than Oskar. How can he stand there so silently and take all that crap? Just once, why can't he fight for himself? *I would love to hear him tell his father to—*

She sat on the edge of her bed, took off her shoes, and threw them against the wall. They fell to the floor with a thud. *It's never going to happen,* she thought, *never . . . unless I make it happen.*

She fell asleep, waiting for Peter, one last tiny tear glittering on her cheek.

* * *

The streets were filled with Christmas shoppers as Kathy walked through sections of Hackensack, looking at one apartment after another. She was discouraged and tired. On an impulse, she decided to go to Brooklyn to visit her mother.

"Hi, Momma. Thought I'd surprise you."

Alice was sitting in the kitchen alone, drinking coffee, smoking a cigarette. "Well . . . well, look what jes' dropped in. Did ya git lost in Joisey or sometin'?"

Kathy smiled. "No, Momma, I've been out looking for an apartment. I can't believe how expensive they are. What's new?"

"Not a goddamn thing. Same ol' crap, different year. Does that meathead know yer out?"

"You mean Oskar?"

"Yeah, the Hitler."

"I guess he knows by now," said Kathy, "but let's not talk about him. I'm sick of him! How have you been, Momma? You look a little tired."

"What's the sense of complaining? Who's gonna listen?"

Kathy felt a pang of pity for her mother. She was right, who was going to listen? She had no one to lean on, never had. The years of hard work and miseries had taken their toll and showed on her face. She looked old and haggard.

"Wanna cup of coffee?" Alice asked.

"Sure, Momma." There were so many things Kathy wanted to tell her, but as they sat together, sipping coffee, Kathy decided her mother had enough problems of her own—and it wasn't like she would be sympathetic to Kathy's, anyway.

* * *

It was late in the evening when Kathy got home. Hanna sat alone in the living room, reading, and didn't look up. Kathy hesitated at the doorway, then walked down the stairs to the workshop. Oskar looked up, said nothing. Kathy hugged Peter. "Hi, honey."

He buzzed her nose. "Where did you go?"

"I thought I'd go see my mother."

"How's your mother?"

Oskar lifted his head and stared at Kathy. Still, said nothing.

"All right, I guess. Her age is starting to show." She looked at the work spread out on the bench. "Are you going to be long?"

"No, I'm just about finished."

Peter knew Kathy had been apartment hunting, but they decided not to say anything to his parents until they were ready to move. Besides, Oskar had been in an exceptionally good mood lately, and they wanted to

103

keep it that way. Even Kathy's job hadn't appeared to upset him. Peter attributed his sunny disposition to the upcoming holiday visit from Janice, the prodigal Daughter.

Kathy almost forgot about her. She hadn't heard her name mentioned in over six months. She had other things on her mind, and to her, Janice's visit had no significance only insofar as it kept Oskar quiet.

CHAPTER 14

1969

"Merry Christmas!" Alice shouted, her arms extended in greeting. She hugged them with a warmth unusual for her. "It's about time. I've been waitin' for ya. Come in . . . come in."

Peter smiled at her. "I'm sorry we're late."

"Late?" She guffawed. "Fer Christ's sake, you're about ten years late. But what the hell, yer here and that's what counts."

"You're right, Momma. Better late than never!" Kathy chirped.

Alice closed the door and herded them into the living room. Peter arranged the presents on a long wooden table in front of a bay window, around the small tree decked out in tiny silver bells, old-fashioned wooden ornaments, and tinsel.

"I remember these!" Kathy exclaimed, fingering a little wooden sleigh hanging from the tree. "I haven't seen them in years!"

"Ya ain't been *around* in years," Alice reminded.

"No more big trees, Momma?"

"Nah, what's the sense? Ain't nobody 'round. They're too damn much trouble jes' fer me." She turned. "C'mon Peter, I need yer help in the kitchen."

Kathy trailed along. Alice had the kitchen table set with her best dishes, careful not to put out any chipped plates. She had starched her red linen napkins and tucked them in the water glasses. In the center of the table, a bottle of Moët champagne chilled in a silver-plated ice bucket. Alice beamed as she lifted it from the bucket and handed it to Peter.

"This is the real stuff." She pointed to the label. "I figured I could splurge fer it, 'cause it'll probably take youse guys another ten years to come fer another Christmas dinner."

With a loud pop, Peter sent the cork flying through the air, narrowly missing the kitchen light in the process. A champagne mist sparkled around their faces as they clinked the glasses in a toast. Kathy took a sip and noticed a fourth setting at the table. "Is someone else coming?"

"Yes," replied Alice, a toothy grin on her face. "It's a surprise."

"Is it Anna?" Of all her siblings, Kathy missed Anna the most.

"Nope."

"Who? Please tell me, Momma!"

"It's Freddie."

"Freddie?" Kathy exclaimed. "My brother Freddie? Momma, I haven't seen Freddie in over ten years! How wonderful! What's he been doing?"

"Not a helluva lot. When he got out of the service, he bummed around awhile, then got married and I didn't hear from him fer a long time. Now I guess he's got some problems wit his ole lady, so he called me. Seeing' as how I'm the closest he has to a mother." Alice thought a moment, then added, "Ya don't mind, do ya?"

Kathy was arranging a cheese tray when Freddie arrived. "This is my brother Fred," she informed Peter happily and turned back to Freddie. "This is my husband, Peter!"

Freddie extended his hand in a hearty greeting. Kathy looked at him, realizing how little she knew of her oldest and only half-brother. She did not remember ever living with him, nor did she remember his blue eyes. His hair, once shocking orange, now graying at the temples, made them look bluer. Of course, he'd put on a few pounds, but who hadn't? "It's really wonderful to see you, Freddie. You look terrific."

"Let's eat," Alice interrupted. "Ya can admire each other later. I don't want the turkey to git dry."

After years of Hanna's German delicacies, Alice's Christmas dinner of turkey, the mushroom dressing, and the pumpkin pie covered with walnut-orange topping tasted exotic and was excellent. Getting reacquainted with Freddie was a joy, and even Peter looked to Kathy as though he was having a good time. He seemed more relaxed, she thought, more himself than when he was in Oskar's home.

After dinner, she offered to help clean up, but Alice wouldn't hear of it. "Go talk to yer brother, I'm used to doin' things myself."

Because they enjoyed their visit so much, they lost track of time and stayed longer than anticipated. Kathy expected Oskar to be furious, her full stomach tightened in the accustomed knot as they waited in the darkness for a bus to take them home.

To their surprise, the house was dark and silent. Like two teenagers sneaking home after a late date, they tiptoed down the stairs to their room.

Kathy switched on the bedside lamp, her newest acquisition since she got a job, and had started to take off her clothes when she heard the familiar rustling sounds. Oskar entered, unsteady on his feet, his eyes glassy. He had been drinking.

Peter spoke first. "I . . . we thought you were in bed, Father. The house was so quiet."

"Of course it's quiet. Who's here for me to talk to? You?" His short, stubby finger pointed to Kathy. "Her? Certainly not your mother, she's been asleep for hours."

"Did you . . . can I get you something?" Peter asked, his voice anxious.

"No, I just can't sleep. I need someone to talk to. I want Katherine to come with me."

Peter's mouth opened in speechless protest.

Kathy recoiled on the bed, looking at her husband. "Peter, make him leave me alone."

Peter mumbled, "He only wants someone to talk to."

She cried out again, "You know goddamn well that's not all he wants!"

"I just want to talk," Oskar whined. "Just for a little while."

He seized her arm, pulled her from the bed. She stumbled, and Peter helped her up, pleading, "Go with him, Kathy. It's Christmas."

She felt trapped, defeated by his look of gratitude.

She took a deep breath, her mind already whirling with schemes to lull . . . to pacify Oskar. *It will be over soon,* she reminded herself, *the light is at the end of the tunnel.* As she exited the room, she turned to glance once more at her husband, searching for an answer to the question she had no answer for: *What makes me love him so?*

She heard Oskar close the master bedroom door and saw him reach for his cigarettes. She felt his weight as he sat on the edge of the feather bed, next to her, and placed his hand gently on her shoulder. "Katherine, you're the only one who understands me. Talk to me, please, for a little while." He blew out a puff of cigarette smoke.

Her response was tart. "Why don't you talk to your wife?"

107

"She's not good for me anymore. Her heart is made of stone, and she doesn't understand anything. I think she's getting senile."

Kathy looked into his face, his eyes brimming with the maudlin tears of a drunk's self-pity. She turned away.

"Katherine, did you know I willed my father's death?"

Shocked, she quickly turned back to him. She couldn't believe her ears. Oskar had never talked about his parents. "I hated his guts," he continued, "because he destroyed everything I ever loved—my mother, my papier-mâché, my life."

"What's a papier-mâché?"

"It's moistened paper that can be molded into beautiful things, but my father called it child's play. Every time he caught me making something, he ripped it to shreds. My beautiful creations . . . he destroyed!" Oskar angrily stubbed out his cigarette.

"Sometimes," he continued, lighting a new one, "I would wait until my father went to sleep and hid them in the cellar. I don't know how," he shook his head wonderingly, "but somehow he always found them."

Suddenly, he began to laugh, a loud, raucous laugh. "Katherine, did you know I almost became a priest?" Kathy couldn't help but laugh with him. "Yes, it's true! My father thought I should get some religion, so he locked me up in a Catholic seminary.

"On my thirteenth birthday, he came to visit me, and the first thing he did when he entered my room was to rip my papier-mâché airplane from the ceiling, throw it to the floor, and stomp it till it was nothing more than a garbage pile." Oskar's elbows were on his knees, his hands covering his face. He was crying. "I cursed him; we had a terrible fight. I told him I wished he was dead" He stopped talking, the memory too painful. Kathy leaned closer to hear. "On his way home, he had an automobile accident and died." When Oskar lifted his face, his cheeks were wet with tears. "I willed it, Katherine, and it happened. I killed my own father." He began to sob.

Kathy was touched by his pain and put her hand on his shoulder, but his loss of control was momentary. When he lifted his face to her again, it looked as it always did when he was in a vindictive, punishing mood: eyes pinched, nostrils flared, lips pursed. "But he deserved to die!"

Oskar lit another cigarette, leaned back on the pillow, and blew smoke rings to the ceiling. "Katherine, I always wanted us to be happy when we were together. I don't want you to choose between me and anyone else. I believe you can have everything you already have and me, too. You can have it all! I don't understand why you fight it so. It's just adding one more dimension to your life. Wat is wrong with that?"

"Oskar, I . . ."

"Life should include all kinds of dimensions," he said as he stubbed out his cigarette. "Most people, however, don't have the courage to embrace it. I don't want a commitment from you Katherine: I want love and respect. I need that . . . everyone needs that."

He reached for her and pulled her into his arms. "Let me hold you just for a little while."

His breathing became slow and regular. When she looked down at him before slipping out of his bed, he was fast asleep.

The smell of liquor and smoke still lingered on her body as she lay down in her own bed. She knew the more she gave, the more Oskar would demand of her. She looked down at her husband, sleeping so peacefully. *It's our duty, we owe him* . . . he told her that often, but now, she thought, it was over. She thought about it for a long time before falling asleep. In the morning, she would tell Peter her decision was final, irrevocable. Tonight, she lucked out, but she would never take that chance again.

When she opened her eyes, Peter was leaning on his elbow, watching her, his fingers playing with the wisps of hair at the nape of her neck.

"Good morning, Honey. I'm sorry about last night. I tried to wait up for you, but I guess I fell asleep. What time did you come back?"

"Three," she said. Her voice was flat.

"I . . . I guess Oskar felt a little neglected, you know, with it being Christmas and all. I know he was really disappointed that Janice didn't come." Peter hesitated, then added, "I guess it was partly our fault, too . . . I mean, for leaving him to go to your mother's, and staying so long. I can't help feeling guilty."

As he droned on about his guilt, some kind of momentum began to grow inside of Kathy. All of a sudden, she felt very angry. Her voice seemed to explode.

109

"You know, Peter . . . last night I stayed awake a long time, thinking. I made a decision, a promise to myself." She sat up and looked him in the eye, her face set in a frown of determination. "I will *never* be used again! Listen to what I'm saying: if your father ever lays a finger on me again, if he ever touches me again, I promise you, I will *leave this house*—with or *without* you!"

CHAPTER 15

1970

Shortly after Christmas, Hanna slipped on the ice in the backyard and broke her leg. When Oskar was informed his wife would be unable to travel for six weeks, he told her to rent a room near her job, because the family couldn't afford to lose her wages for that length of time. Hanna's boss at the sewing factory was kind enough to offer her a room and a ride to work.

Kathy was assigned the job of running the household in Hanna's absence. After work, she had to hurry home and cook dinner, which left little time for apartment hunting.

She was putting away the clean dishes when the phone rang. Before she could dry her hands, Oskar rushed in, nearly shoving her out of the way, and grabbed it. From the honeyed tone of his voice, she understood it was Janice.

"My dear, how thoughtful of you! And, a happy New Year to you, too! No, I'm not angry with you. Of course I understand." His voice trilled with excitement and laughter. "We have a lot of catching up to do, Janice. I can't wait. Give my love to your mother."

He hung up and turned to Kathy. "She'll be here in May when school lets out. She may stay the whole summer! Isn't that great news?"

"I can't wait," Kathy replied dryly.

As she walked past him out of the kitchen, he reached out and smacked her across the backside. His hearty laugh echoed in the room.

"Don't get jealous, Katherine. You are still my baby."

* * *

The January winds whistled around the house, blowing the recent snow into a frenzy. Oskar clambered up the front steps. He had difficulty putting the key in the door; leaned against it for support, finally located the keyhole. He stumbled into the dark kitchen, tripping over a wooden chair, and shouted, "Where is everybody? Katherine? Where are you? Come up here this instant!"

No one answered him. He leaned over the top of the stairs and shouted again, "Are you down there, Peter? Is that bitch down there with you? If she is, tell her to come up here."

Kathy and Peter were in the workshop and had heard Oskar come in. Kathy's first impulse was to run from the house, but she knew she wouldn't make it past Oskar on the stairs. Instead, she fled to her room, leaving Peter behind. After that, driven by panic, she was no longer thinking. She crawled under the covers, pulling the pillow over her head, hoping to drown out his voice. His voice did, indeed, become muffled. Then she heard nothing except the pounding of her heart. She held her breath, waited . . . still nothing. Slowly, she pulled the covers from her head—and let out a blood-curdling scream.

Oskar was looming over her.

His eyes, red and glassy, leered at her. His shirt, once white, hung open, exposing his hairy chest. His pants hung below his waist. "Well, my pet, there you are." He pulled the pillows from the bed and threw them to the floor. "So . . . you think you're too good for me, huh? I took you from the slums of Brooklyn, and this is the thanks I get." He grabbed her hair and pulled her from the bed. She screamed for Peter's help as she lashed out; her clenched fist found Oskar's stomach. The blow took him by surprise. No one had ever raised a hand to him before. She jumped from the bed, picked up a chair, and held it before her as a shield. Oskar pulled it away and smashed it against the wall.

Kathy ran from the room, screaming. From the corner of her eye, she saw Peter, his head in his hands, still sitting at the workbench where she had left him. She didn't stop. She ran up the stairs, taking two at a time, pulled open the door, and flew out into the dark street. Suddenly, she heard Peter's voice, "Kathy! Kathy, wait for me!" She kept running, didn't turn around, then heard him again: "Wait for me, Kathy! I'm coming!"

He caught up to her, breathing hard, and circled her in his arms. "I'm sorry, honey," he whispered, "so sorry."

They walked, huddled close together against the cold.

CHAPTER 16

1970

Kathy opened her eyes, looked out of her apartment window, then at her husband still asleep beside her, and snuggled closer to him. Since it was Saturday—and a misty gray one, the kind of weather she hated—she didn't have to leave their warm bed. It had been three months since they moved into an apartment of their own, and although she knew Peter missed his parents, she also knew he was happy here.

The apartment was an efficiency; one very large room with a small kitchen. Peter had built a wooden bookcase to divide the big room, which turned it into almost a three-room apartment: bedroom, living room, and kitchenette. They had sealed cracks, spackled walls, and slapped on a fresh coat of paint. The floor of the living room was covered with a discounted blue shag rug and furnished with what Kathy called 'early scrounge:' a blue love seat and matching rocking chair from a thrift store; a small color TV with a three-legged swivel base—a housewarming gift from Alice; and a gorgeous coffee table Peter made out of an old wooden door. But Kathy's favorite new possession was the queen-size bed. It had legs! And satin sheets!

The thought of making love on them excited her, and she rolled even closer to Peter.

"These sheets are slippery," Peter complained without opening his eyes, but he was smiling.

"Don't they feel wonderful though?" she chuckled, kissing his chest. "You feel much better," he said, pulling her close.

.To love and be loved—the ultimate, she thought happily as she surrendered to him.

Later, as they lay side by side, it occurred to Kathy that their lovemaking had taken on a new meaning. Their love still felt fresh and filled with hope for the future, but now it was deepened by the experience of all they had been through together. No price was too high, she thought, as long as she had Peter. She couldn't imagine, nor would she want, life without him.

She rolled over and cupped his face in her hands. "Peter?" she whispered, rubbing her nose against his.

"Hmmm?" He was half-asleep again.

"If I had but one wish, do you know what it would be?"

"Tell me."

"I'd wish to have you as my very own, until the day I die." She kissed him, and everything felt right with the world.

The loud ring of the telephone startled Peter out of his slumber. He focused his eyes on the clock next to the bed; it read nine thirty. Languidly, he reached for the phone.

"Hello?" His voice was still husky with sleep.

Kathy curled close and put her head on his chest. He toyed with her hair as he spoke.

"Mother?" He cleared his throat and quickly sat up. He had not spoken to her or Oskar since their move. "How are you?" He listened to her reply.

"I really don't know, Mother. Does Father know you're calling?" He listened some more.

"Sauerbraten." He sounded interested. Kathy had tried several times to make it, but her efforts had yet to come close to his mother's. "I'd love to, Mother, but I don't know if we can make it. Let me check with Kathy and I'll call you back.

"Don't, Mother, please, let me talk to Kathy. I'll call you back in a few minutes, I promise…" Kathy knew Hanna was crying.

Peter put the phone down and leaned back on the pillow without speaking. Kathy waited, but when he said nothing, she broke the silence. "If you want to visit your mother, it's all right with me."

Peter looked at her with gratitude. "You won't be angry with me?"

She smiled. "I won't be angry. I've been there myself, remember? I know what it's like to miss your mother."

"Come with me," he pleaded.

"I think it would be better if you went alone. Maybe next time."

He reached for her and pulled her back into his arms. He began sprinkling her with little kisses. "Please?"

Kathy tried to resist.

He kissed her breasts. "For me?" he begged. "Won't you do it for me?"

She started to squirm. "I think you're taking unfair advantage of me, Mr. Kunz!" she protested.

His tongue was moving down her stomach. "What can I do to change your mind, Mrs. Kunz?"

"Keep going," she whispered. "I'm sure you'll think of something."

* * *

The next evening, hand in hand, they walked up the front steps of the Kunz family house. Before they had a chance to knock, Oskar opened the door, grinning, arms outstretched. "Come in, come in. We've been waiting for you. It's so good to see you."

The warm greeting—as though they had just returned from a long vacation; not a hint of rancor—caught Kathy off guard.

Oskar threw his arms around Peter, patting his back, a big, toothy smirk on his face. Over Peter's shoulder, he eyed Kathy but made no move to embrace her. Hanna came running from the kitchen into her son's arms. She gave Kathy a mirthless smile but did not speak to her.

"My son, it's so good to see you!" she cried. She stepped back to look at him. "You've lost weight! Turn, let me look at you."

Peter laughed. "I haven't lost a pound, Mother."

King ran down the hallway, barking his approval. Kathy quickly knelt to greet him, snuggling her head next to his, and scratched his ears. King licked her face and swatted the flies with his tail. *Well, someone is happy to see me,* Kathy thought, *even if it is only the dog.*

"Dinner's almost ready," Hanna said, her face rosy with delight. She put her arm through Peter's and led him into the kitchen, leaving Kathy behind with the dog.

The kitchen table was set with the Kunz family's best linens and dishes—just like it had been for Ingrid's long-ago homecoming. The table was set for five and, standing in the back of the room with King, Kathy wondered who was coming to dinner. In all the years she had lived there, they had never had guests to dinner—other than the strange women Oskar

115

periodically brought home. On those occasions, Hanna, feigning illness, would excuse herself and sleep in the attic bed. In the morning, she would serve Oskar and his guest coffee and doughnuts in bed.

"Sit," Oskar commanded. "I'll get the beer." He brought out two bottles, flipping the caps off so carelessly the beer spilled onto the starched white tablecloth. He waved Hanna over to blot it dry.

"So much has happened, Peter," he said, "I don't know where to begin. I've been so busy. Business is really great. I want you to come over tomorrow, so I can show you what I've been doing. But today—" he paused and raised his bottle in a toast— "we drink."

Kathy was about to protest that she had nothing to drink when she heard unfamiliar footsteps in the hallway. She turned and saw a woman enter the kitchen. Without needing an introduction, Kathy recognized Carola. Oskar's home movies showed her as a buxom brunette with long hair, but now her hair was platinum blonde and short, and she was about twenty pounds lighter, her complexion still flawless. Kathy understood the urgency of Hanna's call.

Peter rose.

"Vell, vell," Carola cooed, eyeing him. "So this is Peter. You must forgive my English, eez not so good, but . . . you are more handsome than your fodder." She pinched his cheek approvingly and turned. "And this is Katherine, of course. I've heard so much about you." She winked. "We have much in common, you and I . . . yes?"

The blood rushed to Kathy's face. "I'm pleased to meet you," she said, forcing a smile.

"Enough, enough," Oskar interrupted, showing signs of impatience. "Peter and I have lots to talk about. Would you like a beer, Carola?"

"*Ja.*"

"I'd like one too, Oskar," Kathy said.

"Of course, my dear. I'm sorry. I forgot you drank beer. We haven't seen you in a while." His voice was pure acid.

At dinner, Oskar sat between Hanna and Carola. In spite of her professed difficulty with the language, Carola was talkative, vivacious, and aggressive—everything Hanna was not. Kathy could see why Oskar was taken with her.

"How long do you plan on staying in America?" Kathy asked as Hanna prepared to serve coffee.

"I am leaving next week. Six weeks with one man eez enough!" Carola's laughter was hearty.

Kathy watched Hanna, the perfect hostess, circle the table, filling the cups, serving the Bavarian cream pie. Not once during dinner had Hanna acknowledged or spoken to her daughter-in-law, yet she carried on an amiable conversation with a woman who, for the past five weeks, had slept in her bed with her husband.

The next morning, Peter went back to working for his father. His argument against Kathy's misgivings was: "Let's face it, I haven't been able to find a steady job in three months. We've got to pay the bills somehow. Anyway, it's just temporary. As soon as I get something permanent, I'll quit."

* * *

Kathy came home early one day and found Peter stretched out on the couch reading the newspaper. As she pulled the key from the lock, she said, "What are you doing home so early?"

He sat up and put down the paper. "Father went into the city to order a bed, so I skipped out early."

"A bed?" She closed the door behind her. "Why?"

"For Janice. Oh. Didn't I tell you? She's finally coming. I think Memorial Day weekend."

"Boy," Kathy observed as she put down her purse, "she must be hot stuff if Oskar is springing for a new bed. We slept on that legless thing for five years; she can't sleep on it for a few nights?"

She sat on the couch next to Peter. He put his arm around her and kissed her forehead. "I guess he's trying to make up for a lifetime of absence."

"I wonder."

"What?"

"Nothing." Kathy's throat was tight with pity for the girl.

117

CHAPTER 17

1970

Janice was due on the noon flight from Chicago.

A look of concern clouded Oskar's face as the last of the passengers disembarked. Suddenly, a young, slender brunette with long, flowing hair appeared at the top of the ramp. Her facial features bore a strong resemblance to Oskar's.

She hesitated, looked out at the waiting crowd, lifted a duffel bag to her shoulder, and began to slowly descend the metal steps.

"There she is, there she is!" Oskar shouted, waving his arms. "Isn't she gorgeous? Janice!"

She saw him and waved. Oskar ran to meet her with outstretched arms. He swept her off her feet and twirled her, like a child, in the air.

"My dear, I'm so happy to see you." He held her at arm's length, admiring her. "I'm so delighted to meet you at last."

Janice's fair complexion was rosy with excitement. "I can't believe I'm here!"

"Only your nose is your mother's," Oskar effused, "but I think you're your father's daughter, yes?" He kissed her lightly on the cheek.

"My mother has told me that many times." She smiled coquettishly.

"Perhaps too many. That is why I had to meet you. Come," he said, putting his arm around her waist. "Your family is waiting."

Watching from a distance, Kathy thought that it had been a long time since she'd seen Oskar so happy. Janice moved gracefully, like a dancer. Her pale pink blouse, soft and silky, seemed glued to her breasts as the wind pressed hard against them. Her black skirt ended almost as soon as it began, revealing long, shapely legs. A wide belt, cinched tightly, made her tiny waist look even smaller. As she approached, Kathy could see her large, luminous eyes. The strong winds blew her hair around her face, but Kathy couldn't stop looking at her eyes. There was a peculiar translucency about them. As she watched Janice glide closer, Kathy's stomach tightened in a nervous twinge.

118

Janice's dark eyes flashed. "You must be Peter. I would have known you anywhere. I didn't know I had such a handsome brother."

Their eyes met briefly. Peter seemed embarrassed and shifted his weight from one foot to the other. He smiled, without looking up. "Pleased to meet you, Janice, I've heard so much about you."

He put his arm around Kathy's shoulders. "This is my wife, Kathy."

Janice smiled a polite greeting, and Kathy knew the two of them would never be friends.

Hanna was last to meet Janice. She had stood quietly in the background, waiting her turn to welcome her husband's love child. Her expression revealed nothing.

Oskar got bored with the formalities. "Come . . . let us get out of here. We can talk at home."

He had insisted Janice sit in the front, next to him. Peter offered to drive, but Oskar refused; it was his car, he would drive.

He reminded Kathy of a schoolboy on a date: one hand on the wheel, the other on the girl. Janice giggled, a little nervously, as he squeezed her, but from the backseat, Kathy saw in the rearview mirror that her eyes were on Peter.

When they arrived at the Kunz house, Kathy said she wasn't feeling well and wanted to go home. It was obvious Peter didn't believe her. They rode home in silence.

Sleep eluded Kathy that evening. After hours of tossing and turning, she sat up and reached for her pen and notebook. She looked at the empty pages and wrote a name.

JANICE . . . such long hair—eyes like olives—so dark— so penetrating—looks just like Oskar—it's scary. Hate the way she looked at Peter. Thank God she's his sister.

In the weeks and months that followed, Peter's work habits changed dramatically. Sometimes he'd call Kathy to suggest she eat dinner without him; other times he'd say, "I'll grab a bite here. Oskar has a lot of work he needs done tonight."

119

It was a long, hot, and lonely summer. Kathy spent evenings alone, most weekends at her in-laws' house. With growing alarm, she watched a strong relationship develop between Peter and his half-sister.

Normally shy and reserved, Peter seemed to come alive in Janice's company. She was charming and gregarious, easy to talk to and easy on the eye. Both Oskar and Peter were enthralled with her. For Kathy, the apartment that offered the escape she had wanted so badly had become her prison.

* * *

August was especially hot and muggy. In her old pale-blue nightgown, Kathy was preparing for bed when she heard Peter's key turning in the lock. He hadn't come home for dinner in days, no longer even called to let her know she should go ahead and eat without him.

"Nice of you to visit," she greeted him at the front door.

"What are you still doing up at this hour?"

"What's more interesting," she countered, her voice dripping with her mother's special blend of sarcasm, "is what were *you* doing out at this late hour?"

Without responding, he whisked past her and went directly into the bathroom. She heard the toilet flush, and when he came out, she was sitting up in bed, waiting for her chance to say the other thing that was on her mind.

Her voice was explosive. "Peter, are you sleeping with Janice?"

He looked at her, his face expressionless. "Yes, I am."

Kathy bit her lip hard, her throat tight. "*Why?* Tell me, why?" Fighting back tears, she whispered, "Good God, Peter, she's your *sister*!"

His explanation was immediate, matter of fact, and she's heard it before: "Because I love her, and when you love someone, sex is just a natural way of expressing it."

Kathy swallowed hard, trying not to scream. She thought of Hanna and of how she must feel whenever Oskar brought home other women to spend the night in their marital bed; she recalled her own amazement when she learned that Oskar insisted Hanna serve them coffee and doughnuts in bed—"to display your appreciation to our guest for taking care of my

120

needs." She remembered Oskar's lectures on the perils of jealousy, an emotion forbidden in the Kunz household.

"Don't you love me anymore?"

"Of course I do. You're my wife. One has nothing to do with the other."

She stared at him. He reached for her hand, but she pulled away.

"Kathy, let me explain."

"What's to explain?! You just told me you've been screwing your sister. There's an explanation for that?! You're as crazy as your father! Your whole family is crazy!"

Peter grabbed Kathy by the shoulders and shook her. She had never seen him so angry.

"If you'd just listen to me, I'll explain." His face flushed, the veins in his neck engorged, he gripped her arms, bruising her skin. "It's different, I tell you! It's different . . . very different." He lowered his voice and released his hold of her. The look in his eyes had softened. "You are my wife, that's one kind of love. Janice is my sister, that's another kind of love. Do you get it?" He released her, shoved his hands deep in his pockets, and began to pace the room. "You do understand she's not a threat to our marriage, right? I mean if that's what you're worried about. This thing between us is . . ." he paused, searching for the right words, "is kind of like . . . making up for all the years we've missed out on spending together as brother and sister. It's just a way of expressing our love for each other. Do you understand?"

He reached for her hand and stroked it; she was too spent to pull it away. "It's silly to get all worked up and jealous over my sister." He lifted her chin, kissed her chastely. "After all, it's not as if I'm loving a complete stranger. Besides," he added, "she's going home soon."

"When?" Kathy brightened.

"I'm not exactly sure, but her mother wants her home in time for school in September." He didn't sound happy about that.

Later, while Peter slept at her side, Kathy replayed their conversation in her memory over and over, wanting to believe him. He had tried to make her feel as if she were a jealous teenager, angry over nothing. He hadn't been entirely successful. The gnawing in her stomach remained.

121

One thing, however, was certain. She knew she would forgive him, just as Hanna had forgiven Oskar her whole life. She sat up, reached for her pen, and scribbled:

I'll just sit tight and wait it out. After all, he told me she's no threat to our marriage. She's only his sister. Isn't that what he said. Control, I must practice control.

* * *

Kathy dressed with great care, wanting to look her best for Janice's farewell dinner. In the absence of an alternative, she pretended to accept the Kunz family's way of life. Her only hope was in the knowledge that soon, very soon, it would be over. Janice was going back to California; Kathy couldn't wait.

Oskar and Janice were drinking coffee at the kitchen table.

"Hello, hello!" Oskar shouted, grinning from ear to ear. "Please come in. We have some wonderful news! Janice isn't going home, after all. She's going to live with me!"

Kathy's heart dropped into the pit of her stomach.

"We called her mother and she agreed to let her go to school here!" Oskar clapped his hands. "Isn't that wonderful?"

Janice jumped from her chair and threw her arms around Peter's neck. "I'm so happy! I never thought she'd let me stay! I hate my stepfather! All we did was fight. He's such a son of a bitch, I don't know how my mother can stand him."

Kathy watched Peter. Janice was still hanging from his neck. The look of pleasure on his face was unmistakable.

By the time they finally sat down to dinner, Kathy had lost her appetite. Oskar had taken care of everything. Was that a smirk of satisfaction on his face? Of course, as a father, he would be glad to see such a friendly relationship develop between his children. But more than that, Kathy believed, Oskar knew the bond between Janice and Peter was hurting her, and he delighted in it, as a retribution for what he considered her cruelty to him.

Kathy hadn't slept all night. She finally dozed off by the morning, and when she woke up, Peter had left for work and she was running a fever. She called in sick and went back to sleep. Shortly after noon, she heard a knock. She opened the door, pulling her robe closed.

Kathy and Oskar stared at each other over the threshold, both surprised. He spoke first. "What are you doing here?"

"What do you mean, what am I doing here?" She felt foggy. "I live here." She could smell the liquor on his breath.

"Why are you not at work? She was getting impatient now, but pulled her robe closed tighter. "Oskar, what do you want?"

"I'm looking for Peter."

"You came here looking for Peter? I thought he worked for you."

"Well, I sent him to the city early this morning and expected him back by now. I thought maybe he stopped here."

Kathy didn't believe him.

"Well, he's not here."

"May I come in?"

"No. I'm not feeling well."

"All the more reason why I should come in. I can take care of you."

"I don't need you to take care of me. Please go away." She tried to close the door, but his foot was already strategically placed in the way.

"Have you no respect? I drove all this distance, and you're not going to offer me a beer?"

"The last thing you need is *another* beer. Go home, Oskar, you're drunk. It's not that far."

He tried to push the door, but she resisted, throwing her full weight against it. "Katherine, please, it's been such a long time. Let me come in for a little while."

"Go away, Oskar," she hissed, "and leave me alone!" She slammed the door, barely missing his fingers.

He didn't leave. He walked in and out of the building. Each time he came back he shouted louder and was more abusive.

In a panic, looking for Peter, she called the Kunz house.

"Hi, Kathy." Janice's voice was friendly.

123

"What are *you* doing home?" Kathy asked. "I thought you were in school."

"I'm playing hooky today."

"Is Peter there?"

"Yes, he is. Hold on a sec." She heard her say, "It's Kathy."

Kathy was curt. "How was your trip to the city?"

"Fine. Why do you ask?"

"Did you take Janice with you?"

"Yes, as a matter of fact, I did. Why?"

"Well, you should have told your father. There was silence on the other end of the line. Kathy's voice was sharp. "You'd better come over here and get him. He's out in the hallway, making an ass of himself. He's drunk and abusive and I have locked him out. Also, I have a fever."

"Please, Kathy, let him in," Peter pleaded. "I'll be right there."

She walked back to the front door, put her ear against it, heard nothing. Cautiously cracking it open, she peeked out and chuckled at the sight. Oskar was slouched against the wall, his hat tipped to one side of his head, asleep.

When Peter and Janice arrived, Oskar was drinking black coffee at the kitchen table. He had awakened moments before, and Kathy allowed him in, telling him that Peter was on his way.

Oskar appeared embarrassed to let his daughter see him in such a state of disarray. He brushed at his pants, as if trying to iron out the wrinkles, went into the bathroom to wash his face and hands and comb his hair.

Kathy turned to Peter. "Oskar says he came here looking for you. Do you often come home during the day?"

Peter and Janice exchanged quick glances. "No, not often."

Oskar's eyebrows shot up. "What kind of an answer is that?"

"What he means, Oskar," Kathy explained bitterly, "is that whenever he has a chance, they come here and do what you taught him to do: screw in the bed where he sleeps with his wife."

Oskar banged his fist on the table, veins popping in his instantly reddened neck, eyes bulging. "You ungrateful bastard! You knew of my suffering, my needs, and all this time you and Janice have been having sex behind my back?"

Janice's face turned ashen. She had never seen one of her father's tantrums before.

Oskar grabbed her arm. "Come, Janice," he commanded, "let's go home."

"Let me drive you," Peter offered.

"I can drive myself." Oskar's eyes were ablaze. "Janice and I do not need your help. Stay here. Attend to your wife. She is unwell." He pulled his daughter from the room; Kathy could hear her protesting all the way down the hall.

She locked the door, a faint smile on her face.

Distraught, Peter dropped on the couch. "Why did you do that, Kathy?"

"How long did you expect me to keep it a secret?"

"Haven't I been honest with you, sharing all my feelings? Why did you have to tell Father? You knew he would get upset."

Kathy no longer knew where her fever ended, and her rage began. "Is that all you're worried about, getting your *father* upset? What about me . . . your *wife*?! It's been months since you told me she was going home. You don't come home for dinner anymore and don't even call—we just take it for granted that you're not coming. I try to talk to you--you don't listen. I try to get your attention in bed--you've got a headache. I can't do anything right. It's been weeks since we've made love."

Peter looked at her and said nothing.

She paced around the couch, feeling dizzy, her face beaded with sweat. "Do you ever think about having sex with *me*? Or only with your sister now?" Kathy leaned over his shoulder, yelling in his ear. "What am I supposed to do when you don't come home night after night?"

Peter brightened. "Why didn't you tell me you wanted to take a lover? I can understand that."

"Jesus Christ, Peter! Every day you sound more and more like your father!" She threw herself face down on the bed.

Seething with rage, burning up with fever, unable to sleep, she tortured herself with visions of Peter and Janice laughing together, holding hands, making love. She got out of bed and went into the kitchenette with her pad and pen.

I could just scream! Who the hell do you think you are,
Janice? You think other people are sitting around waiting for
you to show up and make hell out of their lives? You are
nothing, and you know it! You make me sick!
How can you expect people not to see through your
selfishness? Don't you realize that they do? Or are you too
dumb! Oh, you are going to school, but if you can't get along
with people, all the schooling in the world will do you no good.
Just look at Oskar! Will he ever grow up? And you are truly
his daughter: taking what you want, when you want, from
whomever you want!!!
Let me tell you this, it is not a threat, but if I ever get the
chance, there are a few scores I have to settle with you. I don't
think I need to mention what. You have a lot to learn, kid! Why
don't you seriously think it all over? Maybe you will find that
you will suffer the greatest loss.

CHAPTER 18

1970

When Peter got to work the next morning, Oskar pointed to a tray of electronic components. "Fix them," he said, got up from his workbench and stalked out of the room. They didn't speak the rest of the morning.

At noon, Peter went up to the kitchen and found Oskar at the kitchen table with a half-empty bottle of beer. Peter got himself a beer out of the refrigerator and sat across from his father.

Oskar broke the silence. "Peter, I really don't feel like talking to you today, but there is one thing I must say. It's very selfish of you to have two women while I have none. It shows your lack of concern for me."

Oskar put the beer to his lips and took a long swig. He wiped his mouth with the back of his hand. "I've been thinking about you and Janice and I have come to a decision." He looked his son in the eye. "She will be allowed to have nothing more to do with you unless she also has sex with me!"

Peter became livid. For the first time in his life, he raised his voice to his father, refusing either to give up Janice or to encourage her to submit to Oskar. The quarrel became so violent that he stormed out of the house.

It was after five thirty when he returned. The house was quiet; he assumed no one was home. Janice's schoolbooks and two empty coffee cups were on the kitchen table, and his mother was nowhere to be seen.

Peter started to walk down the hallway when he heard sounds from his parents' bedroom. Although the door was closed, the sounds were self-explanatory. He was too late. Once again, his father had won.

He wanted to scream, kick in the door, and take his sister from his father's arms, but he hadn't the courage. Instead, he left the house, slamming the door with such force the windows shook, and went home.

Kathy stood at the stove, making dinner for one, used to eating alone. The look on his face alerted her. "What's wrong?" she asked as he whisked past her, threw himself on the bed, and pulled a pillow over his head. "What happened?"

127

"Leave me alone!" he mumbled from beneath the pillow. "I want to be by myself."

Kathy was cleaning the kitchen when the phone rang. When it rang for the third time, she called to Peter, "Are you going to answer it?" He didn't respond. She walked back into the bedroom alcove and picked up the phone.

Her tone was unsympathetic as she threw the phone on the bed, next to him. "Your baby sister's crying for her big brother!"

The conversation was brief, but it got Peter out of bed. When he entered the living-room area with two beers, he was ready to talk.

Kathy listened with mounting rage. "Jesus Christ, Peter, how come it was all right for me to service Oskar, but it's not okay for Janice? I had to do it for years, and I never saw you get upset. All I ever heard from you was, my *father has great needs, Kathy; you're the only one who can help him!* Bullshit! Your father is a goddamn sex maniac and a rapist, who should have been put away years ago. And, except for you and your mother covering for him, he would have been. So now he screwed your sister—what did you expect? He always gets what he wants, and you've let him, for years. You can't stop him now. He's sick, Peter, and you know it! But Oskar isn't the only one in the family who's sick, is he? You all are!"

For the first time in her married life, Kathy spent the night on the couch, tossing and turning in despair. Would it ever end? Could Peter love Janice so much that he'd actually fight for her? Could he run off with Janice to get her away from Oskar? She panicked at the thought of him leaving her. What would she do without him?

Finally, unable to sleep, she walked into the kitchen in search of a pen. She sat at the table and wrote:

So, he was there today. He must have known something would happen. He is lying to me—telling me not to worry about their affair. Well, I was deceived and I shall make up my mind not to acknowledge the whole affair; after all, I am the one he is callous with—and that is not what our relationship was based on at all. He is telling me how open he can be with her, and yet hides so much from me. I'm beginning to realize that things are just not what they seem.

And to think that I've loved him all those years, waited so long and took so much, just to have him! To have him, now I see, is not what I thought it would be. I always thought it would be wonderful to have someone around who wants to be with you, someone to talk to, to understand and just feel good with—someone to enjoy things with. Instead, it's just one day after another, lonesome, the same stale old conversations. His wits pitted against mine, a compromise and struggle. I'll ignore him and not fight or argue about anything.

I have a plan to get my things in order to a point where I can really make the most of my mornings. I'll fix and prepare three dresses to keep aside for emergencies, then get up early each day and get something new ready for that day. I like that idea very much.

I guess I am a little surprised at how easily I can swallow this pill. He treats me as if he were afraid of me, he acts like I am the monster, still, he does what he wants. I guess I am inclined to believe my own eyes—actions speak loudest, and today he has told me via his actions that he does not trust me or believe in me. Today I have decided to stop thinking of our relationship as something special. It is not. I am a wife and I am not treated like one. I will respond accordingly to that from now on. And when I have had enough, I will change it. I know it is only a matter of time. I doubt if I could ever find anyone else. I know I would expect too much from them. I guess there is not much to do but wait until I've had my fill. I must not even try to talk to him anymore. Those days are over. I will not continue trying to make myself understood, or struggle, I'll just wait. I must find a life for myself, just as he does. And for me, things must be worthwhile—for me alone. I'll wait . . . Perhaps in the spring.

In the next few weeks, a sort of apathy overcame Kathy. When Peter came home, she greeted him almost amiably, set food before him, went to bed with him, as though she had been drugged into normal behavior. She had decided that if Peter were still involved with his family by spring, she would get a car and a dog and move to Colorado.

Knowing that Oskar was sleeping with Janice was something of a relief, as Oskar's needs must have taken up a considerable amount of time Janice used to spend with Peter. A strange relationship began to develop between Kathy and Janice. Although they had never been friendly, now that Janice took her place in Oskar's bed, Kathy felt a certain kinship with her, even though their rivalry over Peter's affections continued unresolved.

Once Kathy got to know her a little better, she found it hard to dislike Janice. Brimming with vivacious, youthful energy, Janice had also inherited her father's colorful way with words, and her conversations were witty and articulate. Besides, it was Janice who repeatedly sought out Kathy's company.

One Saturday afternoon, she unexpectedly showed up at Kathy's door. Peter and Oskar had gone to the city, she explained, and she didn't want to babysit Hanna, not that Hanna had ever shown any interest in spending time with her.

"Kathy, let's talk," she blurted, "it's long past time we did!"

Janice sat on the cold linoleum floor in the kitchen, cross-legged, talking long into the evening about how much she hated having sex with Oskar. She had cherished him as a father, but now, as a lover, he repulsed her.

"I especially hate the way he kisses me," Janice said. "Somehow, in spite of all of his brainwashing, I still don't think it's right for a father to kiss his daughter the way he does, all wet and gushy and slobbery and full of tongue. Ugh!"

It was moments like these that Kathy felt closer to Janice than any other member of the family. For a time, they became confidants and Janice confided that she wanted to go back home.

130

CHAPTER 19

1971

One weekend, on the way back home from a family visit, Kathy asked her husband, "Why the puss? Is there something going on that I should know about?"

"Janice is definitely going back to California. She's had it with Oskar. She told me she just can't take it anymore."

Kathy tried to act surprised. "Oh? When is she leaving?"

"She wants to leave before Christmas, but Oskar's having a fit. He's begging her to stay through the holiday. He's been trying to make her feel guilty. He's saying things like, 'How can you think of leaving me right before Christmas?' He's really making a big deal out of Christmas, but I think it's because he's afraid of Janice's mother."

"Why should he be afraid of her?"

"Well, she put him in prison once . . . she might just do it again if she finds out he's been fooling around with her daughter."

Kathy was shocked. "Oskar, in prison? When?"

Peter told her that while his family was living in France after the war, Else, angered at Oskar for refusing to divorce Hanna and marry her, had reported Oskar to the French authorities for his activities as an SS officer in the German prison camps. After being held somewhere in France for over two years, Oskar had escaped and walked back to Germany.

"Have you seen that *O* tattooed under his arm?" Peter asked.

"Yes. He told me it was O for Oskar."

Peter smiled. 'That's what he tells everybody but during the war, all SS officers had to have their blood type tattooed under their left arm. On the battlefield, it ensured immediate medical treatment. You know they were considered to be the chosen few. We are so lucky Kathy; you can learn a lot from him. He is really very, very smart."

Kathy listened, realizing how little she really knew of a man she had known so intimately and for so long.

Christmas came and went. Janice remained. Once again Oskar had prevailed, but the resentment and anger between father and son had reached a boiling point. For the first time, Kathy feared they would actually come to blows.

Her own misery was becoming unbearable. She knew Janice had stayed not because of Oskar but because of her love for Peter. She was now convinced that they were planning to run away together, and her sleepless nights were spent pondering her fate.

* * *

February is usually the nastiest month of the year, but February 1971 brought warmth to Kathy's heart. The mailman delivered a letter addressed to Peter. There was no subterfuge about it: Janice had written her name in the top left-hand corner of the envelope. Kathy turned it over and over in her hands. Surely she had the right to tear it open and read it. Or she could steam it open and re-glue it. But to what end? She put it on the table with the other mail.

When Peter came home, she watched his face as he opened it. To her surprise, when he finished reading, he handed it to her.

Dear Peter:

I can't take it anymore. I want to live my own life. I want to be free of loving anyone. You and Oskar demand too much of me! I want to run away—away from both of you. I do love you, but perhaps not as you love me. I don't know. But I'm not going to let either of you tear me to pieces. I am going back home. By the time you get this, I'll be on my way.

Good-bye, Peter.

Love,

Janice

Kathy handed the letter back to him. "What are you going to do?"

"What can I do?"

Kathy put a comforting hand on his shoulder. She understood his pain, for she had suffered it.

"We can be happy again, Peter," she whispered. "I know we can."

Peter looked at her with hangdog eyes.

She turned and went to the kitchen, her heart thundering. For the first time in months, she felt hope. If a new beginning was in the making, she was going to prepare for it. She put her best linen on the table and chilled a bottle of wine. When she called Peter to dinner, he seemed almost himself. Later, she picked up the unfinished bottle and suggested they finish it in bed.

"That's the best offer I've had all day," he said.

CHAPTER 20

1971

Peter's loyalty to his father had morphed into hatred, perhaps the strongest feeling Peter had ever known yet. He became determined to get away from Oskar. One unseasonably hot day in late March, Kathy came home to find Peter waiting for her. Before she could take the key out of the lock, he lifted her into the air and whirled her around the room.

"What?" she squealed, "What happened?"

"I got a job," he said, his face beaming with pride. "My first real job!"

That spring and summer, Kathy gradually came to feel that she had finally emerged from the heavy wooden trap of her father-in-law's darkness, the tyranny of his moods and needs in that evil house. She had lost much: her innocence, two babies, her ability to trust. To love Peter— that she would do, could not help but do. But she had also learned to take care of herself. More and more, she had found that by waiting and coaxing she could turn her very dependency into unspoken control.

Patience, her eyes seemed to counsel whenever she looked in the mirror, *you're getting your way. Haven't you always known you would?*

She wondered if it was Hanna's way, as well.

With Peter working full-time at an electronics factory, they began to dream of buying a place in the country. On weekends, they went house hunting in the suburbs.

They found their house some twenty miles from where they lived, high on a hill overlooking the Hudson River, in a sleepy little village of Piermont, where large trees and thick shrubs smothered stone cottages, clapboard Cape Cods, and fake-brick ranch types.

It was an old frame house that had been remodeled, to some extent. One large room ran from front to back, opening on the yard surrounded by lilacs and dogwood trees. The ground floor was on two levels, and Peter saw this as an opportunity to create a dramatic sunken den. Back at their apartment, he spent hours sketching out the changes he could make by knocking out walls and putting in archways.

There was one snag—money.

"He's bringing in a good income," Kathy told her mother, "but we need a car and of course, the down payment."

To her surprise, Alice offered to lend them two thousand dollars.

"I didn't know you had that kind of money, Momma," said Kathy.

"I ain't worked all these years for nothin', ya know. But if I lend ya the money, can I come and live wit ya? I could git some kind of a job there, too, ya know."

Kathy had dreamed of living in a house in the country alone with Peter. She felt she had earned it. Still, it was her mother—and they did need the money—so she cautiously replied, "I'll have to ask Peter, Momma. I just don't know."

That evening, she and Peter discussed their financial situation. With some reluctance, Peter accepted the suggestion that Alice come to live with them. If Alice did get a job, she could contribute to the household expenses so Kathy could stop working and help him build his own business, designing and making sets and props for film production companies. More and more, he needed someone to answer the phones and handle the paperwork. Kathy was thrilled.

They took Alice to see the house, and she became almost wistful in her desire to live there with them. The upstairs bedroom that would be hers had a beautiful view of the river. She heard the birds chirping in the trees, a squirrel chased another across the grass, a neighbor's lawn-mower whirred and the scent of newly cut grass rose headily in the afternoon air.

"It could of been different if I'd had a house like this," Alice said.

Kathy could not remember having ever seen her in so soft a mood. For the first time, she began to regard Alice as a whole person—with a childhood, a girl hood, a life of betrayal and sorrow.

"We must get together and make plans," she said

.

CHAPTER 21

1972–73

The muggy heat of July had been blown away by the cool northwest winds of August when a neighbor welcomed them to their new home.

The indoor partitions had been removed; the sunken den Peter designed had come into being, carpeted with bright red plush, mounds of soft, thick cushions scattered around. The room, though small, was a great conversational area, with a circular center table, and a wrought-iron lamp hanging over it. Kathy couldn't wait to host her first party there. She stretched luxuriously. "I feel like the Queen of Sheba."

"If ya come into the kitchen, ya won't feel like such a queen," Alice promised her. "It's a mess."

But the kitchen only added to Kathy's happiness. She thought it was perfect, with a sink in an island counter and a matching green stove and refrigerator. Even a space for a dishwasher had been provided, though it was vacant. That would come later. Alice, however, made good use of the space by storing her tall wooden stool there. Each morning she enjoyed sitting at the counter, drinking her coffee, smoking her ever-present cigarette, grumbling at the cats and dogs she had brought with her from Brooklyn, and watching her shows on television.

Free to make friends, Kathy was quick to make them. One cold autumn morning, she answered a knock at her front door and was startled to see the town's police chief holding an injured puppy. Chief O'Shea had heard the newcomers kept a lot of pets and wondered if Kathy could help nurse the puppy back to health.

A few days later, he stopped by to check up on the dog. "She's doing fine," Kathy reassured him, cradling the blissful puppy in her arms. "The other dogs just love her."

"Thank you for taking care of her, ma'am. That was very kind of you. If there's anything I can do for you, please let me know." He waved good-bye and drove off in his patrol car.

It was good to know she now had the police chief as her friend, especially since Peter's new business frequently took him out of town.

Friends were a luxury Oskar had never allowed, any more than the hope of two people living a simple life together, far from his vicious control. As her world expanded, she felt more and more certain that she was free of him, and her lip curled with the bitter satisfaction of her triumph.

She had earned it. Oskar would never rupture her world again.

* * *

One warm June evening, Kathy and Peter were sitting on their porch. The mock orange was in bloom, its flowers like white stars twinkling in its green foliage, its fragrance lending the air an almost tropical feel. Peter broke the reverie.

"Honey, how would you like a vacation? I have to go to Haiti next month, and I thought you might like to come along."

"Haiti?" Kathy jumped out of her chair and fell in his lap, covering his face with tiny kisses.

"Okay, okay!" He chuckled.

"Are you serious? Can we really go to Haiti?" She pictured herself running across the golden sand and swimming in blue waters, of making love to Peter on the warm beaches, the stars shining overhead.

Peter interrupted her fantasy. "It won't be all play, you know. I'll be working a lot of the time."

"But the thought is so exciting! I can't believe it! When?"

"I don't know yet. We're still working out the details." He stood up and stretched, the bottom half of his blue pajamas peeking out from beneath his paisley robe. He put his arm around her shoulders and said, "Let's go to bed. I'm heading for Boston tomorrow and I want to get an early start. I've got a busy day ahead of me."

Kathy was too excited to sleep. She opened the closet door, the light inside coming on automatically. It was a big closet, twice the size she'd had when they lived in the apartment. She riffled through her dresses, suits, and pants, trying to decide what she would take with her on her vacation, picking out a white cotton sundress and holding it to her, swaying for a moment, her eyes shut, pretending she was already there.

Peter's voice startled her. "What are you doing? Why don't you come to bed?"

She lay awake, thinking about how wonderful things have been lately—the lovely house; Peter happy with his job, her mother so close, and now her first trip abroad! Who would have ever thought she'd get to go to Haiti? Kathy leaned over and whispered to her sleepy husband, "I love you, Peter."

Reaching for her notepad, she quickly scribbled:

HAITI HERE WE COME! I CAN'T BELIEVE IT!

* * *

On the long drive to Boston the next morning, Peter went over the instructions he had been given: the name of the man that he had to work with, the equipment that had to be secured, the circuits that had to be created. Since it was his first major assignment out of town, he was a little apprehensive.

"Hi," said a young woman when he entered the Boston offices of the production company he worked for. "You look lost. Maybe I can help you."

Peter smiled, embarrassed that his nervousness was so evident. "I'm looking for Bill Vaughn. Do you know where he is?"

"Sure, everybody knows Bill," she said with a sassy clip in her voice. "Follow me. My name's Penny." When she turned, he noticed how long her hair was, a shining chestnut cascade that fell below her tiny buttocks. *It's even more beautiful than Janice's,* he thought. *How nice it would look on a pillow.*

Hours later, as he left work, he found Penny waiting for him. The chemistry between them had been instant. When she invited him to her place for dinner, he accepted without hesitation. He met her roommates—two men, one of them a paraplegic. She invited him to spend the night.

The next morning, Peter called his wife and told her he would not make it home for the weekend. "The project is taking longer than expected," he said. "I'll see you sometime late Sunday."

Kathy was disappointed, but her excitement about going to Haiti superseded all else. "Don't work too hard, honey. I'll miss you."

After the call, Peter and Penny drove to Cape Cod.

138

Peter came home late Sunday evening. Kathy rushed into his arms. He didn't return her ardor. Penny's body seemed to glide between them. He couldn't stop thinking of her beautiful hair, her husky laughter; he could still smell her on his hands. He wondered if Kathy could, too.

As they got ready for bed that evening, Peter had difficulty concentrating. "I met a girl at work that I'd like you to meet," he finally said. "She's your age, and she's a lot of fun. I think you'd enjoy her company. Maybe we can invite her to spend a weekend sometime."

"Sure, if you want to." Kathy tried to feign polite enthusiasm, but she really had no interest in some strange girl in a distant city. Her only thought was of her upcoming trip. "I think I'll go shopping tomorrow. I want to get a new bathing suit."

"For what?"

"Don't tell me you already forgot about our trip to Haiti? I haven't been able to think of anything else!"

Since his return from Boston, Peter had thought of nothing but Penny.

He tied the belt of his robe tightly around him and walked to the window, opened the blinds, gazed at the stars dimly shining like small, sad diamonds. He could feel Penny's soft skin against his face, her small, perfect breasts with the upturned nipples under his hand, on his lips. The thought aroused him.

He shot a quick glance at his wife, wondering if she had noticed. He had forgotten about Haiti, but now that Kathy had brought it up, another exciting thought crossed his mind: that long, beautiful mane blowing in the warm Haitian breeze; that gorgeous body under a bikini . . .

"A penny for your thoughts," Kathy whispered as she sneaked up behind him, hugging him tightly at the waist.

* * *

The next evening, Peter said, "There's been a problem with the Haiti trip."

"Don't tell me it's off, Peter, please. I'll be so disappointed."

"It's not exactly off, just pushed back."

"I can wait!" she replied eagerly, happy that her fears were

139

unfounded. "What's the problem?"

"It's something to do with the location. I'm not sure what's going to happen, I only know it's off for now."

"Maybe it's just as well," she said agreeably. "I think I'm coming down with something. I've been feeling really tired the last few days."

When Peter left for Boston the following weekend, Kathy felt almost relieved to be alone—to rest, to plan, and to dream. Even though the summer heat began to take its toll and she felt drained, her spirits were high. *JUST GET ME TO HAITI AND I'LL FEEL LIKE A MILLION BUCKS,* she wrote in her notes.

When Peter returned, he was again anxious to talk about the young woman from work. "It's amazing, Kathy, how much alike you and Penny are. I really would like you to meet her."

"Okay, but could we do it after we get back from Haiti? I've still got so much to do around here, and I'm really exhausted. I don't know why, but lately I feel terrible. I can't wait to get away."

"Speaking of getting away . . ." Peter began, "I hate to tell you this, because I know how much you've been looking forward to it . . . but our trip to Haiti is off."

"Off?"

"Ah . . . what I mean is . . . as a vacation for us. What I'm trying to say is, the trip is back on, but we've been told we can't bring wives. They feel if all the guys bring their wives, they won't work as hard and it may prolong the shooting schedule."

Kathy was stunned. "You can't *mean* that, Peter! Tell me you're joking."

"It's not a joke, honey. I know you're disappointed, but I can't do anything about it. Orders are orders, you know." He leaned over and pecked her on the cheek. "I'm really sorry." Peter continued to talk, but Kathy stopped listening. She began to cry.

"C'mon, Kathy, it's not that bad. I promise I'll take you on a real vacation as soon as we get some extra money. Besides, now that I think about it, it probably wasn't a good idea in the first place. Who would have taken care of the phones while we were gone? You know I can't have your mother do it. I really need you here, Kathy. Six weeks is a long time to leave the business unattended. We can't afford to lose that kind of money."

Kathy shrugged and bit back her feelings. "Oh, I know you're right, honey, but I was really looking forward to it. It would have been a wonderful way to celebrate our twelfth anniversary."

"C'mon, dry your tears. I'll bring you back something special . . .something really special."

* * *

Alice came from the kitchen and handed Kathy a glass of lemonade.

"Ya look like hell," she announced. "Why ya killing yerself? Slow down, will ya?"

"I can't, Momma. With Peter being away, there's so much to do."

"Who sez you gotta do it all?"

"Who else is there?"

"I don't see why ya should be breaking yer ass while that husband of yers is sunning hisself on some beach."

"Momma! I told you he's working. It's not all fun and games, you know."

"No, I don't know. I don't trust a damn one of these guys. I never met a good one yet."

It was too hot to argue. Kathy took a long, cool sip of her lemonade and settled back on the couch. "It's this weather that makes me so tired. The city was like a sweatbox today and lugging all this equipment around was no picnic. I'll be glad when Peter comes back so he can do his own schlepping."

Alice wasn't impressed. "Why dontcha go and lay down? Yer as pale as a ghost."

Kathy agreed and went to bed. Her stomach was so unsettled she skipped supper and asked for milk and crackers instead.

Next morning, Kathy went to see Dr. Roth, the physician who had attended her after the miscarriage. The drive to his office was long, and she couldn't help recalling the horrors of the night preceding her hospitalization.

I mustn't think about that, she chided herself. This is a new day and a new world.

Dr. Roth greeted her warmly. "Hello, Mrs. Kunz! How are you?"

"Pregnant again, I hope," she replied.

She chatted happily while Dr. Roth examined her, telling him that she and Peter now had their own home, that they were going to celebrate their wedding anniversary next month, and that she really hoped she was pregnant, because they were both ready for it. She also told him that Peter was in Haiti on assignment and she was expecting him back in six weeks.

"Well," the doctor told her, "you'll have a nice anniversary present for him when he returns. You *are* pregnant!"

"Momma, Momma," Kathy called as she ran up the front steps. "I'm going to have a baby!"

Alice scoffed. "Big deal. I had ten of 'em."

"Yes, mama, but none more exciting than the first one. You told me so yourself. I can't wait to tell Peter."

CHAPTER 22

1973

"Ya got a card from him in the mail," Alice grumbled.

"Oh, *great!*" Kathy grabbed it from her mother's hand.

"Damn nice of him, considerin' he's already been gone fer four weeks."

Kathy walked away, too engrossed in Peter's card to pay attention to her mother's sarcasm.

Kathy was plagued with morning sickness, but on the morning of August 9, she jumped out of bed, feeling that nothing, not even nausea, could dampen her spirits. It was her wedding anniversary, and, when Peter called that evening, she would tell him the good news. She could hardly wait.

To pass the time, she went to the shopping mall, and found a parking spot on the upper level right near the Macy's entrance. She knew exactly what she was looking for: a new tie tack for Peter. A special gift for their anniversary, she told the salesgirl at the jewelry counter, which she was going to have engraved with the initials "PK."

After supper, she stretched out on the couch with Cuddles, her calico kitten, in her lap, to watch TV and wait for her husband's call. As the evening grew late and she became increasingly restless, she glared at the phone and yelled, "Hurry up and ring already, will you?!"

Alice shouted from her upstairs bedroom, "Go to bed, will ya? If the phone rings, ya can hear it from yer room."

The call never came. But the next day, the mailman delivered a postcard from Peter saying he would be returning home that Saturday.

* * *

When Kathy finally caught a glimpse of her husband among the crowds at the arrivals terminal, she rushed to him, pushing past people, stepping on toes, to throw her arms around his neck, to smother him with kisses. "I've missed you. Let me look at you . . . you've got a great tan." She was breathless. "You look terrific."

Peter removed her arms from his neck. "Don't hang on me, Kathy, I'm tired."

"I'm sorry, Peter. Here, let me help you with the bags."

She tried to take a small bag from him, but he resisted. Instead, he quickened his pace and Kathy had to scamper to keep up with him.

"What's your hurry, Peter? You're not catching a plane."

"I told you, I'm tired," he snapped. "I just want to get out of this airport and get home."

The highway was congested, and driving was slow. Kathy reached for his hand and squeezed it gently. "Honey, are you all right? Did you have any problems with the job?"

"No," he replied, pulling his hand away. "Why do you ask?"

"You act as if something is wrong."

"I'm fine. Just a little tired."

She scooted closer to him. "I have some great news that will pick you right up," she promised, trying to control her excitement. "We're going to have a baby!"

She felt Peter's body stiffen as if struck by a bullet. His mouth was opening and closing, but no words came out. He looked at her, his face ashen. "*A baby?!* Kathy—you can't! Not now!"

"Why? Why not?" she cried.

"Because!"

"Because why? You've got a job, we've got a house, and Oskar is out of our life. I thought you'd be happy!"

Peter turned away.

"Peter, for God's sake, say something!"

"Let's wait until we get out of this damned traffic and get home. I'm too tired to think right now. I have a lot on my mind."

They drove the rest of the way home in silence. As Alice opened the door for them, Peter mumbled a quick goodnight, brushed past her, heading straight for the bedroom, and closed the door.

Alice looked puzzled. She studied Kathy and said, "So? What's wit him? Did ya two have a fight?"

"No." Kathy shook her head. "He's tired. I don't think the job went very well, but he doesn't want to talk about it. Maybe I'll just let him rest and we can talk tomorrow."

"Doesn't he want to eat?"

"I guess he ate on the plane. I don't know, but if you don't mind, Momma, I think I'll just get a quick bite and go to bed early myself. I'm beat."

Peter was asleep. She looked at his body, bronzed by the Haitian sun, wanting to touch him, to wrap herself in his arms. She undressed slowly, then slide under the covers, his breath sweet on her shoulder, tears of disappointment rolling down her cheeks.

She was the first one up and had the coffee brewing when Alice came into the kitchen. Kathy handed her mother a mug.

"Yer up early."

"I couldn't sleep."

"Peter don't seem to have no problems."

"I'm going to wake him and see if he wants breakfast."

He didn't. He rolled over, buried his face in the pillow, and mumbled, "Leave me alone. I want to sleep."

Sometime later, while Kathy was cleaning the backyard, Peter got out of bed, dressed quickly, and slipped out of the house unnoticed.

At noon, Alice and Kathy had lunch, carefully avoiding the subject of his unusual behavior.

Peter returned after five. Kathy was in the kitchen, preparing dinner. "Where have you been?" She tried to keep the hurt out of her voice.

He ignored the question. "Get dressed, Kathy, we're going out."

"What about dinner?"

"We're going out to eat. As a matter of fact, pack a bag, we're going to spend the night at a motel."

Beaming, Kathy rushed into the bedroom, her voice echoing down the hallway. "You don't have to ask twice, just give me a minute to change my clothes!"

As the car left the driveway, she waved good-bye to her mother, slid across the seat, put her arm through his and hugged it close to her body. She was so happy, she failed to notice his sullenness.

The suburban restaurant was large, decorated in faux-frontier style with somebody's concept of early 19th-century posters and red-shaded lamps that cast a ruby glow.

Kathy took a sip of her beer, put her glass down quietly on the wooden trestle table, and looked at her husband, waiting for him to speak.

"Let's have a nice, quiet dinner first. Then we have some things to discuss."

He had had all night to think about it.

"Peter," she said, "I thought you'd be happy that we're going to have a baby."

The waiter came and took their order. Peter ordered a bottle of wine but refused to talk about anything until they had finished eating.

Her joy finally dampened by his sullenness, Kathy said coolly, "I think I've waited long enough. Would you mind telling me what's bugging you?"

He stood up and pushed back his chair, making a loud noise. "Let's get out of here. I'll tell you as soon as we get to the motel."

They drove for miles in silence, looking for a motel with a vacancy sign. By the time they found one, the meal she had eaten felt lodged in her throat. Once in the room, she flipped on the TV and heard the weatherman predicting a storm. As she settled in, Kathy's hands were trembling. Feeling as nervous as a teenager about to make love for the first time, she sat at the foot of the bed, waiting.

Peter paced the room, picking nervously at his cuticles. Not looking at her, he finally blurted out, "Kathy, I don't know how else to say this to you, so I'll give it to you straight. I want a divorce."

She had expected him to try to convince her to have another abortion—which she was prepared to fight him on—but divorce? She stared in disbelief. Finally, her voice, barely audible, squeaked, "A divorce? Why?"

"Kathy . . . I want to be honest with you. I've always tried to be honest with you, and you know that." He sat next to her and put his arm around her shoulders as if to confide in her but kept looking at the floor. "Do you remember me telling you about a girl named Penny? Well. I— I— took her to Haiti with me. We spent—"

Kathy jumped from the bed and, in a wild rage, began to pound him with her fists. "You son of a bitch! How could you do that to me? You knew how much I was looking forward to it, and you took a *stranger*?"

146

Peter grabbed her wrists. He looked into her eyes and said, "She's not a stranger anymore, Kathy. I love her, and I want to marry her."

He could feel her body go limp and released her wrists. Slowly, like a wounded lamb, Kathy crawled to the top of the bed, looking for shelter. She wanted to run away and hide, become once again an invisible child. Instead, she fluffed the pillows, placed them neatly one in front of the other, and laid back deeply into them, eyes closed, trying to erase Peter's words.

"I realize now," he went on, "that you and I were never in love, perhaps in love *with* love, but never *in* love. We were just too young to know."

"Speak for yourself," she mumbled without opening her eyes.

"What we had was different from what Penny and I have," Peter continued as if she hadn't spoken. "I don't want to hurt you, Kathy, and I want to be completely honest with you. I care about you, I really do. That's why I think it's best . . ." He hesitated before saying, "I want you to have an abortion."

His words jolted her to life. "Like *hell* I will!" she screeched. "I will *never* have another abortion! I've waited fourteen years to have a baby, and neither you nor your father will take it away from me."

She jumped to her feet, tears flowing down her cheeks, her voice strong with conviction. "I'm going to have this baby, Peter Kunz, with or without you!!" She ran to the door and pulled it open. She froze! Her mouth opened but no words escaped. At first, she thought she was dreaming. Her eyes opened wide and she knew with certainty she was not. It was her worst nightmare. Oskar was leaning against the wall smoking a cigarette. The sneer on his face made her scream: "NO! NO!" Then with a strength born out of fear, she lunged at him, raking her nails down his face. She ran down the stairs screaming, "You'll never take this baby from me... NEVER!!"

Oskar reached into his pocket for a handkerchief to wipe the blood running down his cheek. For a moment, father and son looked at each other without speaking, then quickly stepped into the room and locked the door behind them.

It was after midnight when Kathy returned home. The taxi driver waited at the curb as she ran into the house to get the fare.

147

Her mother heard her calling. "What the hell is going on?

"Nothing momma, I just need some money."

"What fer? She looked at her daughter's face. "Jesus Christ! Ya look like hell. Where ya been?"

"Momma, please, just get me some money so I pay the driver. I'm sick . . .I can't talk now." She ran into the bathroom and Alice heard her vomiting.

The next morning, Peter came home early and quietly walked into the room. It was dark, but he knew she was not asleep. "Kathy?" He didn't wait for her to respond. "I'm sorry I upset you last night and I've been doing a lot of thinking."

I'm sure you have, she thought

"I know how much you want this baby and I think I have figured out a solution." He sat next to her on the bed, extending one arm across her body. He stared at her for a moment and said softly, "Kathy, before you say anything, hear me out. Will you promise to just hear me out, please? Maybe it won't be necessary for us to get a divorce," he began. Slowly she opened her eyes. "At least not right away," he added hastily. "If you recall, I told you I wanted you to meet Penny. Do you remember that?"

She nodded.

"She's a very nice girl. You're so much alike it's unbelievable." He chuckled, but his laughter sounded brittle and fearful. "I think," he said, hesitantly again, "I really think we should all live together. This way, you can have the baby and I can have Penny."

Kathy rolled away from him, buried her head in the pillow, and began to cry. Did he seriously believe that that was a solution? His words, though muffled, seemed to ring in her ears. *My God, he really believes it can be done.*

"Kathy, are you listening to me? It can work! I know it can if you would just cooperate. I've seen it work! If you love me as much as you say you do, you'll do it. Think about it, Kathy. And if you do . . . I promise not to divorce you."

She pulled the pillow tightly around her head, hoping to silence his words, but she could still hear him. She bolted upright and screamed into his face, "Stop! I don't need to think about it, Peter! The answer is no! I will not allow Penny to live in my house, now or ever! I will never live in another house like Oskar's, not even for you!" She fell back on the pillows devastated, the rest of his arguments a blur.

Sometime later, she got out of bed. She stepped into the shower, allowing the warm water to soothe her hot, almost feverish face. Then, she looked down at her stomach and smiled. She lathered it tenderly and decided she would let Peter feel the baby move. Knowing it was his child she was sure her would love it. Surely, he would change his mind. But she had to do something to get Oskar out of their lives. She remembered Peter's words uttered so long ago: 'the only woman Oskar fears is Else, Janice's mother. She was the one who reported him to the French authorities and had him incarcerated for two years.'

Her spirits began to rise now that she had a plan. She would not tell anyone, including her mother. Instead she would put her plan into action. She wrapped a towel around her body, went into her room and picked up the phone. Her hands trembled as she dialed the number.

"Else, this is Kathy Kunz. It's time you knew what Oskar did to your daughter."

CHAPTER 23

The sense of abandonment that came over Kathy in the weeks that followed promised to become even more intense. While Peter's job now demanded that he do most of his work up in Boston, in his desire to be fair to both his wife and his mistress he also began to alternate his weekends between Boston and Piermont. Kathy never tried to stop him from leaving or asked questions when he returned, but the innocence with which Peter insisted on sharing his experiences with her underscored the cruelty of his betrayal. A gifted artist, he loved to draw, and he brought home studies of Penny posing naked in bed, her long hair streaming over a pillow. He would show them to Kathy, seeking praise for his skills and Penny's charms.

"Isn't she gorgeous? Have you ever seen such beautiful hair?"

At night, Kathy would pour out her anguish in her writing, more passionately and nakedly than she ever had for Oskar's review in the past.

You want me to wait for you to find your answers—to reach your conclusions, but I can't wait. For me it's not worth it. I just can't take it anymore. I am sorry if it makes any more problems for you. I feel so lonely—unwanted—unnecessary—and foolish. Foolish because my dream was a home—a happy good relationship with the one I loved. It isn't possible.

Peter, too, kept a journal, a sort of scrapbook in which he pasted letters from friends and carbon copies of his replies. There were letters to and from Janice, and notes to Penny. He asked Kathy if she would like to see the book, and, apathetically, she agreed. But when she began to read, she felt sick and ran to the bathroom for relief.

* * *

The autumn sun was warm, and a light breeze blew Alice's skirt around her legs. "Git out in the sun," Alice urged Kathy, "and do some

150

work in the garden. Yer as white as a ghost. Why don't ya transplant that dogwood seedling ya been talking about fer weeks?"

Kathy didn't feel like doing anything, least of all gardening in the hot sun. But she didn't have the energy to argue about it, either, so she gathered her tools and began to dig a hole for the tree. As she poked at the dirt, her thoughts, as usual, drifted to Penny. An idea began to churn in her mind. When Peter came home that evening, she said, "Peter, I can't take it anymore. I'm starting to think of ways to kill her." He gave her a look of disgust and walked away. When they went to bed, he rolled over to his side without saying goodnight. Kathy sat on the edge of the bed and wrote frantically:

I will dig the hole deeper, throw bags of leaves over her—pour acid over her—and forget it.

Oblivious to the immensity of the blow he had dealt his wife, Peter appeared to take for granted that life would go on as before, that Kathy would be there to make him dinner, to talk to, to sleep with, to continue answering the phone calls generated by his work. He had become friends with Bill Vaughn, the colleague he'd met in Boston. Whenever possible, they asked to be assigned to the same projects and as a result, frequently traveled together. One such trip—this time, to Cleveland—was imminent.

Over dinner one Friday night, Peter said, "Kathy, when I go to visit Penny tomorrow, I plan to suggest that when I get back from Ohio, we all get together for dinner. I think it's about time you two met. Don't you?"

Kathy still wasn't ready to consent to this idea. "For God's sake, Peter, isn't it enough that you spend every other weekend with her? Do you have to foist her on me, too?"

"If that's the way you feel about it, Kathy, then forget it," he replied, and didn't say another word for the rest of the evening.

Next morning, Saturday, Peter left for Boston earlier than usual. Kathy was awakened by the sound of an engine warming up. She looked at the clock: it read seven. She rolled over and thought, *He just can't wait to get there, can he?* A wave of nausea overcame her, and she ran to the bathroom. Her body awash in cold sweat, she fell to her knees in front of the toilet and vomited. Then, marshaling all her energy, she made her way back to her room, threw herself on the bed, pulled up the covers, and finally fell asleep.

When next she opened her eyes, the sun was shining. She looked out the window. *It's such a beautiful day,* she thought, still slightly nauseous, *there must be something I can do to make myself feel better.* Suddenly, as if struck by a bolt of lightning, Kathy had an idea. She would go to Boston and see Penny. *Maybe she doesn't know I'm pregnant. Maybe, if I show her my swollen belly, it might convince her to stop seeing Peter.* The idea was stimulating; her mood changed almost immediately; she no longer felt queasy. She had made a decision, and now she had to make a plan. She reached for her pen and pad.

Clean house—shop & prepare for trip—leave early Monday morning—take time—have breakfast along the road— wait outside for her to leave house—catch up with her—ask her to sit in car—we have to talk about Peter.

As she wrote, Alice passed her doorway.

"Momma, I'm going to Boston on Monday."

Alice stopped, a bewildered look on her face. "What the hell fer?"

"Well, you know, Peter's been wanting me to meet Penny, so I thought I'd go up and have a little talk with her."

Alice shook her head. "Ya must have rocks in yer head, Kathy. Ya mean to tell me ya gonna drive all the way to Boston in yer condition, jes' to meet that broad? Are ya crazy or sometin'? What the hell d'ya think ya gonna gain by that?"

"I just want to talk to her, Momma, about Peter and me, and I want her to see me pregnant."

"Why, ya think she ain't ever seen no one pregnant before? I think yer nuts, Kathy. I think you'd better go see a shrink! Yer 'n' Peter are two false alarms."

Alice waved her arms in disgust and went into the kitchen for her coffee and cigarettes. Kathy followed. She poured Cuddles a bowl of milk, fixed herself a cup of coffee, carried it into the dining room, and looked out on the patio. The Venetian blinds, which usually covered the door, had been pulled up. As she glanced out, she could clearly see the hole she had dug earlier in the yard.

Kathy's mind began churning again. *If I could bring her here, I could throw her in that hole. But how can I get her to come back with me?*

In the distance, she heard Alice calling, "Kathy, ya deaf or sometin'? What the hell's wrong with ya? Lately, ya never pay no attention to me."

Annoyed by the intrusion, Kathy snapped, "I didn't hear you, Momma. What do you want?"

"I jes' wanted to know if yer gonna go to the mall today. I'm all out of my knitting yarn."

"I'll go later, Momma, after lunch. Right now, I've got lots to do."

She didn't want to forget a thing. She went back to her room and jotted down a few more reminders:

I have to take with me—blankets, leaves, shovel, rake. Check for car—I must get lots of sleep this weekend and plenty of fresh air—then I will be back here Tues. eve—and all will be okay—it would be simpler to just leave things go as they are. If I try to make too many changes—things—other things—will become obvious.

*   *   *

The mall was a brand-new, indoor shopping area with a variety of boutiques lining the outer perimeter of the walkways, anchored by a large Macy's at one end and a Sears at the other. As she entered the building on that early Saturday afternoon, Kathy realized she was having difficulty breathing and walking. Her knees started to buckle beneath her. Her vision blurred; everything darkened, as if someone had just dimmed the lights. The noise around her was thunderous. Crowds of milling suburban shoppers appeared to converge on her with huge, distorted faces like giant caricatures. She became disoriented and frightened. *Why is everyone laughing and making weird faces at me?* she wondered. *What's happening?* She covered her ears with her hands, hoping to drown out the deafening noises. Her eyes darted from walkway to walkway, looking for an escape route. She spotted a wooden bench and tried to reach it, but people kept getting in her way. She was frantic. *How do I get away from them? What do all these people want from me?* She started to cry.

"Are you all right?" asked a kindly voice. "Can I help you?"

"No . . . no!" Kathy screamed. "Just go away!"

"Are you sick?" the woman persisted. "Do you need a doctor?"

"A doctor?" Kathy tried to focus on the voice. "Yes, that's what I need. I need a doctor."

"Do you want me to call someone for you?"

"No," Kathy insisted. "I can call myself."

The woman was skeptical. "Are you sure? Here, let me help you."

"No, no, leave me alone, I can walk by myself."

Shoppers stared. Kathy freed herself from the woman's grip and made her way to the pay phones. She stood breathless, trying to regain her composure. Her hands were trembling as she reached for the phone book. She studied the numbers until they came into focus, then dialed the first psychiatrist whose name started with an A. The phone rang for a long time.

"Hello . . . hello, my name is Kathy Kunz and . . . I'm at the mall. People here are laughing at me. They're making a lot of noise . . . my head is hurting. I'm getting really scared."

"Is this an emergency?"

"Well . . . no," Kathy responded hesitantly. "I don't know. I . . . guess not? It's just the noise . . . it's hurting my head. I can't breathe . . ."

"Go home," the doctor interrupted. "It sounds like a panic attack. You need to rest. If you don't feel better by morning, call me back." The receiver clicked in her ear.

Kathy looked at the phone, puzzled, and slowly replaced it in its cradle. *I guess I must be all right?* she thought. *The doctor didn't sound concerned. Why are they still staring at me? I'd better get out of here. I don't know why I came here in the first place.*

Getting home was a nightmare. Kathy held the wheel tightly, her back erect, her head high. Despite her best efforts, her eyes closed from time to time, which caused her car to drift out onto the shoulder. Other drivers honked loudly in reprimand as they passed. She shook her head frequently, trying to dislodge the weight that seemed to have fallen on her.

Alice was napping. Kathy went to her room and fell into bed. The ceiling whirled about her; then there was total darkness.

By morning, she was too ill to get out of bed. Alice tried to force her to eat, but what little went down quickly came back up.

Monday morning, Kathy called the psychiatrist with the name starting with an A and made an appointment. When Peter came home, she told him.

"Why, what's wrong?" he asked.

"I don't know. I feel like I am going crazy. The strangest things have been happening to me. And this thing with you and Penny is driving me nuts. Every chance you get, you run off to see her. You don't seem to give a damn if I live or die." She looked into her husband's eyes. "Please, Peter, come with me. Maybe he can help us."

"*Us?* What do you mean, *us*? I don't need help. There's nothing wrong with me. You're the one with the problem."

"Then come for my sake, please?"

Peter left the table with a resounding "No."

The next morning, Kathy went to see the psychiatrist alone. She parked her car on the street in front of his house and walked the stone path to the side door to his office. With trembling hands, she rang the bell. The door stood slightly ajar, so she opened it and looked into a small, almost square, windowless room. A brown leather couch, a wooden table and lamp in the corner, and two straight-backed wooden chairs filled the entire space. She sat down, picked up a magazine. She didn't hear the door open on the other side of the room and was startled to look up and see a small, dark-haired man standing before her.

"I've been waiting for you, Mrs. Kunz." His accent was European but not the same as Oskar's.

He took a seat across from her. His smile was warm as he reached for a pad and pencil and said kindly, "Let's start at the beginning. Tell me how I can help you. Is there a particular thing or person disturbing you?"

She wanted to cry out, *It's Penny. I hate her, I hate her, I hate her. I wish she were dead!* But she was afraid.

155

"Tell me about your husband, Mrs. Kunz," the doctor prodded. "Is he your problem?"

"Yes," she said quickly. "After all we've been through, he now wants a divorce." The words began to flow, and suddenly she couldn't speak fast enough. The doctor leaned back in his chair, folded his arms, and listened. She told him of Peter's relationship with Penny, revealed her history with Oskar, and, finally, opened up about the abortions.

"Mrs. Kunz, are you *sure* your husband was aware of your relationship with his father?"

"*Aware?* Are you kidding? He encouraged it! He got angry with me for trying to avoid it!"

"And how did you avoid it?" the doctor asked.

"Sometimes I took long walks, just to get out of the house. Other times, I took the bus to the city to meet Peter. But the more I tried to avoid Oskar, the more he wanted me. Sometimes he would come into my room in the middle of the night, even though my husband was sleeping right at my side and make me come to his room . . . to talk."

The doctor's eyebrows rose. "What was your husband's reaction to that?"

"Nothing. He would roll over and say, 'Let him do what he wants and stop making trouble'."

"Did you have your mother-in-law living in the house?"

"Yes, she lives there, but that's about all."

"What do you mean?"

"She does whatever Oskar tells her to do, without questions. Many times, she's had to get out of bed and sleep on the couch or the spare bed in the attic."

The doctor leaned forward for a closer look at his patient. "Did your mother-in-law ever object to this treatment?"

"Never. I'm sure she doesn't like it, but she's used to it."

"Have you ever discussed your father-in-law's behavior with your husband?"

"Many times. But he just accepts it. That's the way he was raised. No one in the family ever disagreed with Oskar."

The doctor checked the time. The hour was almost over. He stood up, pushed his chair aside, and approached his patient. "Mrs. Kunz, do you think you could bring your husband with you on your next visit? I would like to meet him."

"You want me to bring Peter here?"

"Yes, do you think that's possible?"

"I've already asked him once, but I'll ask again. He said I'm the one with the problem."

"Perhaps if you tell him you were here today and that I've asked him to come, he might reconsider. Would you ask him again, please?"

Kathy nodded. She got up from her chair and straightened her skirt. Her legs felt weak and rubbery. She looked at the doctor uncertainly. "I'll try, but . . ."

"If he won't come, would you ask him at least to call me? If I am going to help you, I must speak to him. I'm sure he will understand."

157

CHAPTER 24

1973

Perched on the edge of her bed, her mind roiling with thoughts of Penny, Kathy picked up her pen:

Early Monday night—leave to go up there—prepare a thermos of O.J. vodka and pills—catch her leaving her house and tell her Peter is in the hospital and we must leave immediately—along the way offer her some "juice"—it should be that simple—meanwhile, have the hole prepared and when I get back—dump her in it, pour acid—cover and forget.

A voice rang out from the other room: "Kathy, ya wanna cup o' tea?"

"Thanks, Momma. I'll be right out."

She left the pad on the night table and went into the kitchen. When Kathy saw Cuddles asleep in her favorite spot on the counter, she remembered she was out of kitty litter.

"I'll be going shopping tomorrow," she told Alice. "Do you need anything?"

"A carton of smokes."

"That's all you ever want, Momma." Kathy was getting annoyed at Alice's chain-smoking, as well as at her failure to follow through on her promise to get a job near the house. "You're a human smokestack." She fixed her tea and, carrying Cuddles under her arm, returned to her room, where she dumped the kitten out on the bed, closed the door behind her, and began to pace the floor. Abruptly, as if she had just received an urgent message, she reached for her notepad and wrote an odd shopping list:

BLANKET, PILLOW
PATHMARK:
    Orange juice

158

Kitty litter
White bread
RENT A CAR
Vodka
Roses
ASK ABOUT SCREWDRIVERS
Comic books?
SLEEPING PILLS
SURGICAL GLOVES—NYACK

The aroma of fresh coffee hung in Kathy's room as she opened her eyes next morning. Her stomach grumbled in protest. Instinctively, she reached for the saltines that had by then become a daily habit.

She lay quietly, hoping the crackers would quell her stomach. They didn't. She bolted from the bed, nearly tripping over Cuddles quietly snoozing on her slippers, ran for the bathroom, and folded into the all-too-familiar pose. Peter came down the hallway and stuck his head in the door. "Can I get you anything?"

Shaking her head, Kathy fell back and leaned against the wall, her face dripping with sweat. "How about some juice? Will that help?" he asked. Again, she shook her head and, slowly, rose from the floor to splash some cold water on her face and neck.

Peter returned to his coffee while Kathy brushed her teeth, combed her hair, and put a light touch of gloss on her lips. By the time she walked into the kitchen, the color had returned to her cheeks.

"I went to see a psychiatrist yesterday," she said matter-of-factly.

"Why?" Peter responded without looking up from his newspaper.

"You know very well why. I can't cope with the way things have become around here." She looked at him pleadingly. "Please, Peter, I'm so confused I can't remember what I'm doing from one moment to the next." Her eyes filled with tears. "Peter? Are you listening?"

He put the paper down. "Yes, I'm listening."

"The doctor wants to see you. He says he can't help me unless he talks to you. Please Peter, come with me. I need your help."

"When's your next visit?"

"Tomorrow."

"What time?"

"Seven o'clock."

"All right, I'll try to get home early." He leaned over and kissed her chastely on the forehead.

Shortly after he left, the doorbell rang. Kathy looked out the window and saw two neighborhood boys standing at the front door with rakes in their hands.

"Hi, Mrs. Kunz," they shouted with enthusiasm, "we're trying to raise some money for the new Little League uniforms. Can we rake your leaves?"

Kathy smiled. "Sure, I've been trying to get my husband to do that for weeks."

"Great! Is there anything else you need help with?"

"Maybe I'll think of something before you leave." They followed her to the garage, where she issued them a few large plastic bags.

"Put the leaves in here and stack them by the side of the house," she instructed. "I'll get rid of them later."

"Thank you, Mrs. Kunz. If you think of anything else, just holler."

Back in the dining room, she once again tripped over Cuddles. "I'm sorry," she said, picking the kitten up. "Do you want to go out? She slid open the patio door to let Cuddles out and noticed the hole. *If that hole were bigger . . .* She called the boys, and they came running. "I just thought of something you can do for me. See that hole over there?" She pointed. "When you've finished raking the leaves, dig it deeper. Make sure it's nice and big. I want to plant a large tree there."

"Don't worry, Mrs. Kunz, we'll make it real deep!"

*   *   *

Peter came home early, as promised, and drove Kathy to the psychiatrist's office.

"Mr. Kunz, your wife has told me a few things about you and your family that pique my interest. I would like to hear what you have to say."

"About what?"

"Well . . . let's start with your father."

160

"My father is a very intelligent, caring man. He has provided me and my wife with a home and support for many years."

Kathy bit her lip but remained silent.

"Your wife has gone into considerable detail describing her relationship with your father. Is there anything you would like to tell me about their association?"

"What would you like to know?"

"Are you aware that they had a sexual relationship?"

"Yes."

"How do you feel about it?"

"It is my father's way of communicating with the people he loves."

"Do you approve of his behavior?"

"My approval is of no consequence. My father has great needs and he does what he has to do to fulfill them."

Although at times defensive, Peter answered the doctor's questions honestly and confirmed all that Kathy had said—until the questions became more personal.

"Mr. Kunz, I understand you have been paying regular visits to a lady friend in Boston. Is this correct?"

Peter squirmed in his seat. "That is my private business, Doctor." His voice was flat.

"Are you aware of your wife's anxieties over these trips?"

Peter glowered at the doctor. "My wife's anxieties are of her own making. I realize her pregnancy makes life more difficult for her. That's why I am here. But I didn't come to discuss *me*—I came here to see what you can do to help *her*."

On the way home, Peter told Kathy he would not go see the psychiatrist again. He sounded angry. "Who does he think he is, prying into *my* personal life? It's a violation of my rights. I'm not the one who's sick, you are."

Kathy continued the visits alone but, it seemed to her, to no avail. Before long, she complained to her mother, "Talking to that doctor is like talking to a stone wall or even worse, like talking to Peter. The only difference is now I have to pay for it."

"It's better than not talkin' to nobody," Alice pointed out reasonably.

161

But Kathy's plans for a trip to Boston continued to fester, and Peter's insistence that she meet Penny wasn't helping, either. He gave her Penny's address and phone number and said, "Instead of going to that quack, why don't you listen to me. I know if you just open your mind and give yourself a chance to get to know her, you'd realize you're getting upset over nothing. She's really very nice. I know you will like her. I don't understand why we can't all live together. It would make things so much easier for all of us."

That evening, Kathy scribbled a few more notes:

FOR TRIP:
Rent a car

PREPARE room nicely

PREPARE:
O.J.
Needle
Jar with chloroform + rag
take change—phone

ME:
gloves
sunglasses
wig
cape
hat

PREP HERE:
diddle telephone
make sure Peter sleeps all night

DIG DEEP HOLE
SACKS of leaves
shovel—rake
Clean house
work on clothes

The next morning, at breakfast, Peter surprised Kathy by inviting her to come along with him and Bill Vaughn on their business trip to Ohio. "It might be a nice change of scenery for you," he said. The thought that he wanted her there was flattering, and she was tempted, but her secret plans overwhelmed her so much she declined.

"All I can do is ask." He shrugged. "I'll probably bring Bill home for dinner tonight so we can get an early start."

When Peter left, Kathy activated her plan. She called a car rental agency, then asked a neighbor for a ride into town. She felt strangely calm, not at all her usual self. She drove the car home and parked it on the street close to her house.

Her mother shouted to her as she came in, "Kathy, Peter called. He said not to wait fer supper. He and Bill might be late so ya should go ahead and eat witout 'em."

"Good, I'm not hungry anyway."

"Ya'd better start eatin'sometin, Kathy. Yer feeding two, ya know."

Consumed with the details of her secret plan, Kathy paid no heed to her mother. She went down to the garage and searched for the rake and shovel, which she placed in the trunk of the rental car. Then she went to the backyard, picked up the bags filled with leaves, and added them to the trunk.

When Kathy returned, Alice sat at the counter eating a hamburger. She shot a questioning look at Kathy's wistful expression.

"What's wrong?"

"Everything, Momma."

CHAPTER 25

1973

Kathy went to bed early.

When she heard Peter and Bill come in, she lay rigid, her heart pounding in her ears. They rambled, it seemed, on and on. At last, she heard them say good night. She rolled over and pretended to be asleep.

Time passed erratically. From time to time, she glanced at the clock. Sometimes, the intervals between her glances seemed long, sometimes short. At two o'clock, she cautiously slipped out of bed, picked up the bundle of clothes and a wig she had left on a chair, and tiptoed into the bathroom. She closed the door quietly and switched on the light. The glare hurt her eyes. Her hands shook as she slipped on an all-black outfit and adjusted the wig, so the long black hair fell closely around her cheeks and lent her a strange, exotic look.

She turned off the light and tiptoed into the kitchen in search of her handbag, which contained her sunglasses and black gloves. She was about to put them on, then decided to leave a note:

PETER,
TOOK A RIDE OUT TO MY SISTER ANNA'S
CALL ME TONIGHT—OK?
LEAVE NUMBER WITH MOTHER IF I AM NOT HERE

She read the note several times. *That should do it,* she thought. *Can't think of anything else that needs to be done.* She picked up the sunglasses and gloves and turned to the hall closet. All night she'd thought about what she should wear; she pulled out a chic red wool cape and a matching red beret and walked out the front door into the dark, chilly air. She pulled the cape tightly around her as she approached the rental car and heard her heart thumping while she waited for the motor to warm.

Kathy felt disoriented. She couldn't decide whether to go to Boston or to Anna's. If she went to see Penny, what would she say? "Hi, I'm Kathy, Peter's wife. I'm sure he's told you all about me." No, maybe, "Hi Penny, Peter's told me all about you. I think it's time we had a talk."

164

Oh God, I'm so nervous I think I'll just scratch the whole thing and go see my sister and the kids. Where are the comic books for the kids? Did I forget them? She turned and checked the backseat. They were there.

She put the car in gear and began to drive, still unsure of the direction. She drove around aimlessly for an hour; as the dawn broke in the east, she turned north on the New England Expressway and saw the dawn break in the east. It was a few minutes after eight when she arrived outside the house in which Penny lived. She rolled down the window, filled her lungs with crisp cool air and waited. She was surprised at how calm she was. *I'm doing this for Peter* she thought. *This is what he wants me to do.* Women entered the building, but none of them resembled Penny. Kathy looked at the picture she held in her hand, which started to tremble. Doubt and fear began to set in. She picked up the picture again: fair complexion, long chestnut hair, round face. Again, she checked the address. Suddenly, a girl walking with a bouncy childlike step, her hair flowing down her back, appeared. She was not wearing a coat but seemed burdened carrying a heavy cardigan sweater, a multi-colored duffle bag that she had thrown over her shoulder and a large brown leather bag. The cool breeze pressed her white long-sleeved blouse against her full breasts. Her long skirt fell almost to her socks and loafers.

Kathy's heart began to race. Quickly, she rolled down her window and leaned out. "Are you Penny?"

The girl stopped, looked, a puzzled expression crossed her face. "Yes, I am."

"Do you know who I am?" Kathy smiled.

"No," the girl replied in a friendly way, "but if you take off your glasses, I might recognize you."

"I'm Kathy, Peter's wife." she calmly replied. "Peter's told me all about you. I think it's time we had a talk."

Penny's eyes slanted at her. Her light, laugh was almost mocking. "Yes, yes, I guess it is."

"Peter wants us to . . . you know."

"Yes, I do know..."

To Kathy's surprise Penny walked to the other side of the car, opened the door, and got in. They were now face to face. Neither spoke for a moment as they surveyed each other.

Penny spoke first. "So, you're Kathy. Peter has told me all about you."

"Oh, really?" Kathy sarcastically replied, "Did he also tell you that I am pregnant?"

"Yes," Penny quickly replied, "as a matter of fact he did."

The girl's tone angered Kathy. For a moment she didn't know what to do. She reached for the ignition key and turned it on with pure frustration. She had no idea what to do next or where she was going. She just followed the early morning traffic. She took a deep breath, needing to find her voice.

"Do you know what it's like carrying the baby of someone you love and having him cheat on you?"

"Yes, I do," Penny replied candidly, "I was once pregnant myself."

Slowly, the hard look on Kathy's face softened. "Really? Where's the baby now?"

"I don't know," she replied with no sign of sorrow, "I gave him up for adoption. I was going to have an abortion but, by the time I made up my mind, it was too late."

Kathy's response was loud and swift. "Well, I am not going to have an abortion! I am going to have this baby!" Her voice was shrill as she raised her voice even louder.

"I have no intention of giving up my life with Peter after 12 years of marriage for your relatively twelve minutes with him!" Her face was red with emotion: "HE'S MY HUSBAND AND HE'S GOING TO STAY THAT WAY!"

Penny's mocking laughter surprised her. "Kathy, if that's what your worrying about, you can forget about it. I'm not looking to get married."

"You're not?"

Penny continued in a calm and soothing voice. "No! I'm not! I'm a very independent person. As a matter of fact, I've never done very many permanent things in my life. I just don't like anyone taking me for granted or tying me down." She laughed knowing her words were true. "I guess, I am just a wanderer."

Kathy couldn't believe what she was hearing. *Is she lying to me? What then, does she want from Peter? Maybe I'm worrying about nothing. Peter was right when he said I would like her.*

Kathy and Penny looked at each other and shared a laugh. "Do you make it a habit of going around stealing other people's husbands?"

"No. Can't say that I have." Penny replied. "I've never been married; too busy moving around. I've lived in seven places in the last nine years. I am just a wanderer. So, you have nothing to worry about Kathy. Peter is just another friend who keeps my juices flowing."

Juices flowing? Kathy smiled wondering what Peter would think of that. *I bet he doesn't see it that way.* She turned to look at the young girl seated next to her feeling confused. She seemed so friendly, so sincere. *Could this be for real? Maybe, she is just putting me on.* Have I been driving myself crazy for nothing? Peter's words began echoing in her ears: "Go meet her. . . you will like her. . . we can all live together."

Suddenly, she turned to Penny, "I think I'd better tell you something. Peter has had a serious accident at work and is in the Rivervale Hospital in Ohio. What do you think about us going to see him? He's been saying for some time that we should all get together and I'm beginning to agree with him. This way," she added with a smile, "we can all get a better understanding of things. What do you say we surprise him?"

Penny's laugh was infectious, and Kathy laughed too. "Are you kidding? He'll drop dead of shock." Penny leans back in her seat, puts her arm over the seat and turns to study Kathy. "You know, that sounds like fun. I told you I'm a wanderer. But first I'll have to call the office and then you'll have to take me home because I have no money with me."

Waiting for the light to change, Kathy pressed further. "No problem, I can lend you some money if you really want to go. We'd first we have to stop at my house in Piermont to pick up a check. Then, we could take the morning shuttle to Ohio."

Penny looked at her in amazement. "You're really serious, aren't you?"

"Why not, it was Peter's idea that we meet."

"I can't believe I'm doing this." Penny's hearty laugh revealed her white teeth and little laugh lines at the corner of her mouth. "This sounds like fun. I haven't been to Ohio in ages. I can't wait to see the expression on Peter's face. But first I have to call my boss. I'll tell him I'm sick and need a couple of days." Her voice was excited.

Kathy quickly turned the car towards the highway, stopping at a roadside phone booth, and waited for Penny to compete her call.

She got back in the car, relaxed and happy. The two women began chatting as if they were old friends reunited.

Penny was eager to tell Kathy about her former boyfriends, including two men named David, one of whom had a heart attack and was now in a wheelchair.

"Right now," she said, "I'm going to night school to become a welder."

"Why a welder?" Kathy asked. "Don't you like your job?"

"Yeah . . . it's all right. But I told you I get bored easily and I think it would be fun to be a welder." She chuckled at the thought. "As a matter of fact, I'm supposed to go to class tonight." She pointed to the duffle bag she had thrown in the back seat. "That's why I'm carrying that. It's got my tools in it."

Kathy hadn't slept for almost twenty-four hours and her feet were beginning to swell. The long drive had drained her. She began to look for a stop.

"There's a look-out up ahead, Penny. If you don't mind, I'd like to stretch my legs. They're getting a little stiff. Maybe, if I walk around a bit, it will help."

"I could use a pit stop myself," she replied.

Kathy pulled over to the parking area and slowly got out, legs throbbing. Penny leapt out ahead of her and into the ladies' room. Kathy watched her with envy, thinking, *no wonder Peter is attracted to her. She's so full of piss and vinegar.* She rubbed her swollen belly and waddled to the rest area. When she came out, she noticed Penny leaning precariously over the edge of the cliff. She saw Kathy and shouted, "Come over and look at this view! It's breathtaking."

When Kathy came up behind her, an ominous thought crossed her mind: *one push would do it.* A frown crossed her face. Horrified at the thought, she tried to smile but the expression on her face hadn't escaped Penny's attention.

"Are you alright? You look a little funny."

168

"I'm alright now that the circulation is coming back. Being pregnant isn't all it's cracked up to be. The two women smiled knowingly at each other. "I've got to go back to the ladies' room, I just realized I left my bag there. I'll meet you in the car."

"Don't rush on my account. I've got all day."

Kathy found her bag still hanging on the back of the stall door. She searched through it for something to soothe her throbbing head. She quickly took two aspirins using her hands to cup the cold water. She splashed the water on her flushed face. *What was I thinking? It could have been so easy. One push and my troubles would have been over.* She began questioning her own actions. *Am I doing the right thing bringing Penny home? Oh God, I don't know what I am doing!*

When she walked out of the building, she shielded her eyes against the glaring sunlight. Penny was leaning against the car, waiting. "You look a little pale. Are you all right? Do you want me to drive?"

"I'm fine but we'd better get going. It's getting late."

As they turned to get in the car, a dog ran wildly across the grass and under the cars. His white hair, caked with dried mud, looked almost brown. He looked as if he had been hit by a car. Penny spotted him first. "Oh Kathy, look. That dog is hurt."

Kathy stopped. "No, he's alright. Someone's probably dumped him off here. I don't know how anyone can do that to a helpless animal. It makes me sick. She bent to the ground and called him; he came running. "He sure is dirty." She stroked his head. "I'd love to take him home, but Peter would kill me."

"Why? How many pets do you have?"

"Well . . . altogether, counting cats, we've got ten."

"Ten? My God! I guess you're right."

"We'd better get going," replied Kathy with a wry look on her face. "We've got a long ride ahead of us."

She pulled out of the parking lot and turned on the radio. Loud music filled the car and Penny began to hum.

The aspirins took effect and Kathy felt better. The color returned to her cheeks. She settled back for the long drive home and offered Penny a drink. "I've got some juice in the thermos, if you'd like some."

"No, thanks, Kathy, the coffee was enough for me."

They chatted awhile and then fell into comfortable silence. Kathy thought, *I really can't figure her out. She's really a nice person. I wonder what she wants from Peter. Sex?* She smiled to herself and thought *maybe I should introduce her to Oskar! Oh, would he love that! That bastard, why did I have to think of him?* Almost involuntarily, she found herself telling Penny all about him and their sick relationship.

At first, Penny listened silently. But after a while, it became apparent that she knew. Kathy's temples throbbed again. Finally, she asked, "Did Peter tell you about Oskar and me?"

"Yes," Penny replied quickly. A small smile spread across her face. "He tells me everything."

Kathy's anger reached new heights. *How dare he? That son-of-a-bitch! How dare he tell her of my personal life. He tells her things Oskar told me never to tell anyone!* Her blood pressure was starting to rise. *Is she so much better than me? Is this the honesty Peter talks about, or is it betrayal?* Kathy was no longer thinking, overtaken by abject terror. All she could see was the deep hole in the back yard.

A silence fell over the two women.

When they drove up to the house, dark clouds had formed overhead, and a light drizzle was falling. Kathy asked Penny to wait in the car while she put the dogs away. She rushed up the steps to the front door.

"Momma," she called. "Will you put the dogs in the pen? We have company."

"Who?" Alice shouted.

"Penny."

"Penny?" Alice's voice was angry. "What the hell are ya bringing her here fer? Are ya nuts or something?"

Ignoring her mother's remarks, Kathy helped her usher the dogs into the pen and beckoned Penny in.

"Lo," Alice grunted when introduced. She turned away muttering loud enough for them to hear, "Two nuts waitin to get screwed." She walked into the kitchen, filled the teakettle and slammed it on the stove. She pulled out the tall wooden stool that she kept under the counter, lit a cigarette and blew billowing puffs of smoke into the air.

Penny followed Kathy into the living room, her eyes roaming. At the far end, the dining room table was cluttered with papers, books, and pencils. Cane chairs, four in all, were pushed under the table. Two calico cats slept comfortably, undisturbed by the visiting guest. The venetian blinds had been pulled to the ceiling, allowing unobstructed visibility through the sliding glass door, which led to the rear patio. As they entered, a distant lightning stroke illuminated the room. Kathy turned on the television.

"Why don't you watch T.V. for a while? I've got to lie down; my head is killing me."

Penny plopped into the over-stuffed chair, putting her feet on the ottoman. It felt comfortable after the long drive. "Great, I didn't miss the soaps." She looked at Kathy and said, "You look like you could use some rest."

Kathy walked past her mother, who gave her an angry glance, as she went into her room. The bed groaned under the weight of her swollen body. She was exhausted but sleep eluded her.

Her mother's hostility had upset her, and fears of Peter's reaction gripped her. She was having difficulty breathing so she clasped her arms under her head and took long, deep breaths. *What will Peter think? Will he think I'm crazy? Why should he? He's the one who suggested it. Maybe I should have waited until after the baby was born. Now this will give him an opportunity to make a comparison.* She rubbed her swollen belly. *I look so fat and she. . . God, why didn't I think of these things before I brought her here?*

She got up and began pacing the floor, crisscrossing the room. She saw herself in the mirror, her eyes red-rimmed, her face pale, her wig off center. She pulled it off and threw it across the room. She opened the door, looked down the hall and saw her mother's angry face puffing on a cigarette. She was so restless she couldn't decide what to do. She picked up the pad from her nightstand, found a pen and slowly with deliberate, forceful strokes wrote:

WAIT TILL SHE FINISHES HER CIGARETTE

Wait for what? She paused, looking at her pad. She had no idea why she wrote that. She had no clear idea of anything. The only thing she knew for certain was that her head was about to explode.

171

She looked at the clock. It was only three in the afternoon. She heard the toilet flush and her mother's footsteps in the hallway. Quickly, she opened the door and motioned for her mother to come in. Kathy whispered, "Momma, I've got to get out of this house for a while. I need time to think. I'm going to take a ride to the mall."

"Yer goin' to the mall, huh? Ya been riding all day, now ya wanna ride some more? Are ya outta yer mind, or what? What the hell's wrong wit ya? Ya bring this dumb broad home wit ya and now ya wanna stick her wit me. Why don't you just go to bed? Ya look like death warmed over."

"That's just it, Momma. I can't sleep. I'm too keyed up. Maybe if I get away from her, I can think more clearly."

"Jesus Christ! Why don't ya just make up yer mind. First ya bring her here and now ya want to get away from her. What the hell am I supposed to do wit her?"

"Nothing. Just let her watch television. You can start supper. I won't be long."

In Kathy's absence, tension between Alice and Penny grew. Penny sensed the old woman's hostility and became uneasy, no longer content to sit and watch television, she aimlessly walked around the house looking at pictures on the walls, peering into Kathy's bedroom, walking in and out of the bathroom. She became impatient and decided to make a phone call. She looked around and saw a telephone hanging on the kitchen wall. She picked it up and dialed the operator. Nothing happened. She hung up and dialed again.

She turned to Alice. "What's wrong with the phone?"

Alice's voice was a sneer. "Ain't got no idea."

Penny picked up the receiver again. "Hello? Hello? Can any body hear me?"

Angrily, she slammed the phone onto the cradle and looked at Alice, "Do you know the phone is out of order?"

"I don't know nothin, I jist live here."

Penny returned to the living room and threw herself into the chair resigned to watching television. They spent the rest of the afternoon in complete silence, occasionally casting suspicious glances at each other.

Two hours later, Kathy's car pulled into the driveway. As she opened the door, Alice grunted, "What the hell took ya so long? I got supper waitin'."

Kathy brushed past her into the dining room. The table was set for three. Alice turned the gas off under the vegetables and slammed the hamburgers on a hot iron skillet. They sizzled immediately, sending smoke flames up to the ceiling.

Kathy's stomach grumbled. She realized she had not eaten solid food since the previous evening.

"C'mon Penny," she called, "Let's eat." Penny did not respond. "I'm starving, aren't you?"

"No, I don't want to eat,"

"You haven't eaten all day."

"I'm not hungry."

Kathy sat at the table and began preparing her plate. "Well, come and sit with us and have a drink. There's a thermos of juice in the fridge."

Penny got up. "Okay, I'll have a drink, but I don't want anything to eat." She opened the refrigerator, took out the thermos and poured the juice into a glass. She took a sip and immediately spit it into the sink." She said, "It tastes funny! I really don't want it anyway. I'm going to watch television." As she walked back in the living room she said, "Did you make the shuttle reservations yet?"

"No, not yet." Kathy replied. "But we have plenty of time. Anyway, you don't need reservations. They have shuttles leaving daily from New York,"

After dinner, Alice piled the dishes in the sink and left the greasy skillet on the kitchen stove. She sat on her stool observing Kathy and Penny as they watched television in the living room. Her cigarette smoke hung like a cloud over the counter. She felt old and tired, used up. She wondered what was happening to her daughter. She could see the anxiety building up, the look of panic in Kathy's eyes.

By ten-thirty, Kathy couldn't keep her eyes open. "I'm going to bed. I'm beat." She stretched, pulled herself off the couch and told Penny to sleep in her mother's room. "My mother will share mine. I'll take the animals in with us, so they won't bother you."

Penny nodded.

About eleven-thirty, the ringing of the telephone woke Kathy out of a sound sleep. She rushed down the stairs into the playroom to answer it. She knew it would be Peter. Her heart pounded wildly. *Should I tell him Penny is here sleeping in Momma's bed? No, I can't, it will spoil the surprise. What would he say if I told him we were going to see him tomorrow? I'm so nervous; I don't know what to say—*

"Peter, how nice of you to call!" Her voice was tight and controlled.

"Are you all right?" he asked. "You sound funny."

"I'm fine. You just woke me up."

"Oh, I'm sorry. I just wanted you to know I got here all right. I got your note this morning. Sorry I missed you."

He talked briefly about the job, but Kathy cut him short, fearing she would reveal her secret. "I'll talk to you later, Peter, I'm just exhausted tonight."

"Okay. Sleep tight."

"Good night. I love you."

When she returned to her room, Alice was awake. "Who the hell's calling at this hour?"

"Peter."

"Did ya tell him yer girlfriend is sleepin' in my bed?"

"No."

"Did ya tell him yer going out there tomorrow?"

"No, I want to surprise him,"

"Surprise him, huh? Yer the one who's gonna be surprised. I don't understand you two. Yer two false alarms. Neither one of ya know what the hell yer doin'. Are ya really gonna go to Ohio tomorrow wit that broad?"

Kathy began to cry. Her shoulders shook. "I don't know what to do. Help me Momma, please, I don't know what to do."

The sound of her daughter's sobbing softened Alice. "Aw, come on now. We'll think of something in the mornin'."

A few minutes later Alice rolled restlessly in her bed. She reached for her cigarettes. The pack was empty.

"Kathy," she whispered, "are ya sleeping?"

"No."

"Would ya go in my room and git me a pack of cigarettes? I don't wanna go in there wit her there."

"Jesus Christ Momma, can't you go one night without cigarettes?"

"No, I can't."

Kathy got up and tiptoed into her mother's room. The dim light from the hallway she could see the dresser. As she reached for the drawer, she heard Penny's startled voice. "Who's there? What do you want?"

"It's only me," Kathy replied. "I'm getting a pack of cigarettes for my mother. Go back to sleep."

Kathy awoke the next day with another bout of morning sickness together with an overwhelming feeling of nervousness. She heard her mother in the kitchen and slipped into her robe and slippers, then joined her. The cat was sitting on the counter eating leftover food; the supper dishes with hardened and dried vegetables clinging to them were still piled high in the sink. The iron skillet, gray with congealed grease, remained on the stove. Suddenly, bile rushed to Kathy's throat. She covered her mouth, ran into the bathroom, and vomited. Her body was dripping with sweat. She dragged herself back to her bed, exhausted.

When Penny opened her eyes, the sun was shining. She looked out the window into the back yard and stood quietly for a moment, admiring the fall colors. She was eager to leave but didn't want to be alone with Alice in the kitchen. She had heard Kathy in the bathroom, but the house had again grown silent but for the shuffling of Alice's slippers. Penny dressed—she didn't have a change of clothes, so she slipped into the skirt and sweater she had worn the day before. She stood before the mirror and brushed her long hair, twisting it into a thick bun, securing it with straight pins high on the crown of her head. She looked at her reflection in the mirror and smiled, amused by the thought of Peter's face when he saw her. She wondered if he would be pleased that she and Kathy had finally met. She reached for her scarf, tied it around her hair and left the room.

She glanced at the clock as she entered the kitchen. It was seven-thirty. Alice sat on her stool smoking, her coffee cup before her. Her greeting was cold. "If ya want coffee, help yerself. It's on the stove."

Penny cast a glance at her. "No,' she replied, "but I would like some juice, please."

"Suit yerself. There's some juice in the fridge, in the thermos." She blew smoke into the air.

Penny opened the refrigerator, picked up the thermos and shook it vigorously. She took a glass from the overhead cabinet, poured herself a drink, took one sip and immediately spit it into the sink.

Alice looked over her shoulder at her. "What's the matter?"

"It's bitter."

"So, don't drink it."

Penny put the thermos in the sink and walked into the living, pacing the floor.

"Sit down or git out of my way," Alice hissed at her. "I wanna watch my shows."

Penny heard the toilet flush and knew Kathy was up. She checked the hallway and noticed the open door. Kathy was on her knees, vomiting. "Just give me a few more minutes," she said without looking up. I'll be alright." She pushed herself to her feet, ran cold water in the sink and splashed her face, trying to shake the grogginess from her head.

Penny watched for a moment then moseyed back to Alice's bedroom. She began throwing her belongs into her duffle bag. She picked it up and throwing it over her shoulder, briskly returned to the living room. She dropped the bag next to her chair and plopped herself down to wait.

Kathy dressed slowly. Her arms felt heavy as she adjusted her wig, her stomach sour. Her hands trembled so badly she was unable to tie her shoes. Throwing them angrily against the wall, she searched the closet for another pair. Then she began a fruitless search for a $350.00 check. She opened and slammed drawers noisily.

"Momma," she shouted, "have you seen a check lying around? I don't know what the hell I did with it and I need to cash it this morning."

"Did ya look in yer pocketbook? Ya got everythin but the kitchen sink in there."

Kathy yells back. "Look on the dining room table, will you? Maybe I got it mixed up with the tax papers."

As the two women shouted to each other, Penny stared impatiently at the kitchen clock that read 'eleven ten' and wondered if she was ever going to leave. She turned her back to Alice and slumped into the chair, mumbling inaudible words of disgust.

Her grumbling annoyed Alice. "What the hell are ya saying? If yer talkin to me, speak up so I can hear ya!"

"I'm talking to myself," Penny replied without turning her head. "Just talking to myself."

"I don't need to take yer shit. I got enough problems of my own."

Penny glared at her, turned back to the television, kicked off her shoes and curled her feet under her, preparing for another delay.

"Did you find it, Momma?" Kathy shouted. "It's got to be here somewhere."

Kathy slammed the bureau drawer closed and stood up waiting for her mother to respond. Suddenly she was aware of scuffling noises. For a moment she listened. Then she ran down the hallway to the kitchen, eyes wide in disbelief. The two women were on the floor struggling over a shiny object that Alice held with both hands. Penny was on top of her, trying to pull it from her grip.

"Stop it, Stop it!" Kathy screamed as she pulled at Penny's clothes. "Leave her alone! What are you trying to do to her?" She began pummeling Penny's back with her fists, but the blows had no effect. Kathy wrapped her arms aground the girl's waist and marshaling all her strength, tried to pull her off, screaming, "Get off of her! Get off!"

Suddenly, Penny turned and bit Kathy's arm drawing blood. Kathy screamed. "You bitch, you little bitch." Her eyes were wild as they searched the room. The iron skillet still sat on the stove. She reached for it and slammed it against the side of Penny's head, a blow that echoed like a drum throughout the room. Stunned, Penny shook her head to clear the sound from her ears but maintained her tight grip on Alice. Kathy swung wildly, striking Penny again and again. One blow caught her on the side of her nose. Blood spurted down into her mouth and onto Alice's back. Penny screamed, loosened her grip and Alice fell to the floor. Alice rolled over quickly, jumping to her feet, brandishing the object to which she had so desperately clung: a hammer. Penny was dazed, her eyes barely focusing as she looked up from the floor to see Kathy and Alice standing over her. Kathy still had the skillet in her hand, Alice the hammer. An overwhelming feeling of panic seized her, and she ran for the front door. She managed to open it, but the screen door was locked. Pounding it with her fists, she dislodged part of it and tried to climb out, but Kathy and

Alice were on her again, pulling her back, leaving clumps of her hair on its jagged edges.

"You bitch!" Kathy shouted and slammed the door shut. "Now look what you've done!"

Penny tore herself free and ran towards the back door, but Kathy blocked her way. The girl dodged around the dining table with Kathy in pursuit. A dog ran through the room and tripped her. She clawed out at Kathy, grabbed at her hair and fell to the floor with a thud, holding Kathy's wig in her hand. A throaty, ominous laugh escaped from Kathy's lips, her eyes dilated with excitement. Penny panicked. She leaped up and staggered against the table sending dirty plates and coke bottles crashing to the floor. She ran to the patio door, managing to slide it open. She thrust her upper body out, shouting, "Help! Police! Somebody help me!"

But Kathy and Alice dragged her back. Kathy pulled her by the hair, by then matted with blood. Alice tugged at her clothes and closed the door. Penny broke free again and ran staggering around the rooms, the blood from her scalp blinding her eyes, knocking over furniture, splattering walls. Her screams were piercing.

"Shut up, you little shit!" Kathy shouted. "Do you want the neighbors to hear?"

Suddenly, Penny fell to the floor in a motionless heap. The silence seemed to bring the two women to their senses. Alice shrank away, backing into a corner. Kathy stood staring at the figure on the floor. She became aware that her blouse was sticking to her chest. When she pulled the fabric, it felt wet. When she looked at her fingers, they were red. Again, she stared down at Penny, who didn't stir. Was she dead? A terrible upwelling of joy and horror coursed through her. She tried to remember the past few minutes, but they were all a blur. She felt the heaviness of something that she was holding in her right hand and slowly brought it up before her eyes. Blood was congealing over the hardened grease on the iron skillet. Kathy swayed and sank to her knees.

* * *

The sun was unseasonably hot at eleven thirty a.m.

Mario Pelligrino, in a white T-shirt and overalls, was pouring a cement walk on his new home. He was sweaty, having to work fast if he wanted to finish before lunch. He quickly leveled the cement, pushing his rake back and forth, his mind on the lunch—he should have started the job sooner. He thought he heard a woman scream in the distance, but it didn't make him slow down. As the screams became louder, though, he stood up and listened. It was an unmistakable cry for help, coming from his neighbor's house only two doors away. He dropped his rake and ran to the neighbor's patio door. By the time he reached it, the screams had stopped.

Through the window he saw his neighbor standing in the middle of the room, seemingly frozen into immobility. Her eyes were dilated and glassy. Blood was plastered on the front of her pale-yellow blouse.

He saw her slowly raise her right hand, in which she was holding a heavy iron skillet, mottled with congealed blood. She stared at the skillet and seemed to study it.

Blood was fingerprinted on the walls and windowsill, even smeared on the glass pane through which he peered. Pictures hung askew. Broken china and crystal had fallen and shattered around the dining table.

He realized there was another woman on the floor who was dazed but trying to get up.

He quickly ran to the front of the house and pounded on the door.

His neighbor, Kathy Kunz, angry and distraught, opened the door. She raised her arms to shield her eyes from the glaring sun.

Mario stood stunned. He saw the young woman sitting in the middle of the floor reach for him, her face and hands covered in blood, her plea for help barely audible.

His eyes darted back to Kathy, who screamed, "Mind your own business!" and slammed the door in his face.

Shaken, Mario raced up the hill to his house to call the police.

179

Top: Peter and Kathy Kunz. Bottom: Oscar Kunz

Top: Kathy and Baby Cara. Bottom: Hanna as a young entertainer

Alice Jackson

CHAPTER 26

1973

When Chief O'Shea arrived at the Kunz house, he went straight into the kitchen to call an ambulance. The kitchen phone was out of order. He ran downstairs to use the extension in the playroom. As a frequent guest in the house, he knew where everything was.

When he returned, he persuaded Kathy to go see her doctor. "If you don't care about yourself," he admonished, "think of the baby. You've been through a terrible ordeal."

"My doctor's in New Jersey."

"Give me the number, I'll call him for you and get you a cab."

While they waited, Chief O'Shea asked, "Kathy, tell me what happened. Who was she, anyway?"

"She was Peter's girlfriend, that's who she was!" Kathy snapped. "She tried to kill my mother!" Her voice trembled. "She was on top of her. I couldn't get her off . . . I had to do something!" She started to cry.

"Take it easy, Kathy. Maybe we can talk later, after you come back from the doctor's. Right now, I think you should rest. I'll be at the station all night, so, if you feel up to it, stop by."

The chief turned to Alice, who had sat quietly on her stool, lighting a fresh cigarette from the butt of the last one. "Are you all right?"

"Yeah, I'm fine."

"Do you know how all this started?"

"Well. . .yeah."

"I'd like you to tell me about it later, okay?" soothed O'Shea. "Right now, I think it's important for you to have your arm checked—it looks pretty badly bruised. By the way, Kathy, give me Peter's number, I'll have to call him."

Alice refused to go to the doctor's, so Kathy went alone. She had the cab wait while the doctor dressed her arm. He assured her that the baby was fine and that she had no serious injuries.

*   *   *

The Piermont police station is located on the first floor of an old brick building in the center of town. Two large American flags, one on each side of the white double-door entry, lend credence to a mild feeling of patriotism in the community. In the park a few blocks away, an old cannon serves as a monument to fallen heroes.

Kathy parked her car on the street in front of the station. The sound of her low-heeled shoes echoed on the plank floor, kicking up dust as she headed for the chief's office at the end of the hall. She could smell his cigar smoke wafting out of the open door. When she walked in, O'Shea was leaning back in his swivel chair, his feet on the metal desk, cigar in hand, talking on the phone. He removed his feet from his desk, smiled at her, and waved her in.

"I'll talk to you later," he said to the caller and hung up. The police chief stood up and delicately tapped the cigar in the ashtray, extinguishing the burning tobacco. "How are you feeling Kathy?"

Touching her arm, she smiled. "Doctor says it's nothing serious."

"Good. I'm glad you're here. I've spoken to your husband and he's on his way home. If you're up to it, I'd like you to give me the details of what happened today."

O'Shea called in a court reporter and Kathy told her story, explaining how Peter had asked her to befriend Penny, and that the purpose of Penny's visit had been to seek out a basis for such a friendship. She couldn't understand, she said, why Penny had attacked Alice. She had done what she had to do to protect her mother.

Kathy sounded calm and rational. The chief wanted to believe her. She was his friend, and only weeks earlier he was urging her to run for mayor of their small village after the baby came.

Kathy waited until the statement was typed, read and signed it, and then went home.

The place was a mess. Someone had righted the overturned chairs, but they weren't in their usual places. Splotches of dried blood covered the kitchen floor. Peter was not home.

"Momma!" Kathy called.

Alice's harsh voice issued from her upstairs bedroom. "What?" Kathy found her sitting alone, smoking. "Are you all right, Momma?"

"Yeah, I'm fine. The police have been here all afternoon askin' lots of questions and takin' pictures. I left ya some supper on the stove."

"No, thanks." Kathy walked across the hall to her room and sank onto the bed, shivering. *I didn't try to kill her,* she reassured herself. *Did I? I was just protecting Momma. I could never kill anyone. I nurse puppies to health.* A frightening thought crossed her mind. *What if they think I did?* She jumped to her feet. The notes! They could be misconstrued. She needed to destroy them.

She picked up her notepad with shaking hands and tore away the pages until a clean white sheet looked up at her, calming her down. She tore the pages into tiny pieces and threw them into the wastebasket, then lay down on the bed and fell asleep from sheer exhaustion.

It was dark when she awoke. She sat up and switched on her bedside lamp. It was five minutes after ten. She heard familiar sounds in the driveway. Even though she felt stiff and cold, she rushed to greet Peter at the door.

"Peter, I've been waiting for you! It's been so awful!"

He pushed her away, his eyes glinting with anger. "What did you do?!"

"I didn't do anything, Peter! It was her! She tried to kill Momma!"

"What was she doing here?"

"I invited her here so we could all get together and talk. You said you wanted me to meet her."

His voice was cold. "I didn't want you to *kill* her!"

"I didn't try to kill her, honest! She came at Momma with a hammer. I was only trying to protect her. She was so strong. . . I had to do something!"

Kathy threw her arms around Peter's neck, needing to hold him, wanting to know he believed her, but he pushed her away with such force that she fell to the floor. She grabbed his legs, clung to them, crying, "Please, Peter, you must believe me!"

He looked down at her, his eyes ablaze. "Why did you have to hit her so many times?"

"I don't remember hitting her at all! It was like a bad dream, a nightmare! When I woke up, the police and the neighbors were staring at

185

me. Then I saw her bleeding. I never saw it before, I swear Peter. I never saw it."

He pulled himself free and stalked away, leaving her huddled in the middle of the floor.

"Please, Peter, don't leave. I need you."

The bedroom door slammed.

Suddenly, a feeling of sorrow and deep anger overwhelmed her, a culmination of a lifetime of rejection, abandonment, and frustration. She curled into a motionless ball—and then she was an invisible child once again, with her oversize glasses slipping off her nose, ugly and unloved, her brothers and sisters laughing at her. She remembered her father sleeping in the hallway, the smell of liquor like a cloud hanging over his head.

You never gave me a chance to make you understand! she silently cried out to Peter. *Don't you know how much I love you, have always loved you, still love you?*

She began to rock back and forth. How could things have gone so wrong when she tried so hard? Is it over? she thought. Have I lost Peter for good?

Then darkness engulfed her.

* * *

When Kathy opened her eyes and looked around, the house was silent. The lights were on. The gilt hands of the sunburst clock on the wall showed it was past midnight. She was still on the living-room floor, shivering from the cold. With a groan, she raised herself and waddled down the hallway.

Peter was lying on the bed fully dressed, his hands clasped behind his head, eyes open, staring at the ceiling. He didn't speak. She took off her shoes and crawled under the quilt.

She had a nightmare. The devil was pulling her into a whirlpool, the dark water sucking her downward. She struggled to keep her head up, calling, screaming for help. Suddenly, her body in a cold sweat, she bolted upright. She tried to focus her eyes on the clock, straining them in the dark. It was three o'clock. She heard a noise, which frightened her, and she turned to call Peter. He wasn't there.

She walked quietly down the steps to the basement. A thin line of light underscored the garage door. Kathy opened it and peered in, her hands flying to her mouth to muffle a gasp.

The garage floor was strewn with garbage. Kneeling in the middle of it, Peter was stuffing scraps of paper into his pockets as he rummaged through the piles of trash. He looked up; eyes wide.

"What are you doing?" she whispered.

"Go back to bed," he said flatly. "You've done enough for one day."

Kathy wanted to run at him, arms flailing, to smash his face. Instead, she staggered up the stairs and back to her room. She switched on the light. The wastebasket was empty.

She heard her husband's car backing down the driveway, and knew he was gone.

*　　*　　*

She had not heard from Peter in over a week. She called his parents' house, but there was no answer. She tried again, later in the evening and Ingrid picked up the phone. Ingrid, who used to be her friend, sounded cold, distant. Kathy had intended to pour out the whole story to her, confide in her, and solicit her help. But Ingrid told her dryly that she didn't know where Peter was and offered no further assistance. Kathy understood that Ingrid's loyalty to her brother superseded any feelings she might have for her.

After filing a missing-person report at six o'clock in the morning of November 1, Kathy, who hadn't slept all night, got into her VW, and headed toward New York City. Twice she narrowly missed being hit; other drivers honked angrily at her. She drove randomly around the city, looking for Peter's truck. Eventually, she turned homeward. When she turned off the thruway, she stopped at the Piermont police station to see if they had any information on Peter's whereabouts.

Chief O'Shea was an unhappy man. A cigar clenched tightly between his stained teeth, he contemplated the folder before him and watched Kathy wobble down the hallway to his office.

At first, he had believed the incident would fade away by itself, and he had done his best to encourage both women to forget the matter. But Peter's discovery of the notes made it impossible. Penny was in the Nyack Hospital with a concussion and had initially been reluctant to file charges against Kathy or her mother. But she had reconsidered once she had learned of the content of Kathy's notes.

Looking troubled, O'Shea rose slowly from his chair. The wooden floor, warped from years of abuse, creaked as he came around the desk. Kathy rushed to him, breathless. "Have you found Peter yet?"

The chief shook his head and placed his hand on her shoulder. "Mrs. Kunz, you're under arrest."

He read her the Miranda rights and informed her the arraignment would probably take place within the next few days. Then he handed her a card, which read *Gilbert McCormack, Esq.*

"I think you'd better call him now. You need some good legal advice."

The hurt, blank look on her face disturbed him. He watched her dial the number and wondered if she understood the gravity of the situation. He doubted it.

"Please sit down, Mrs. Kunz," he said formally, indicating a chair across from his desk. "Were you able to reach Mr. McCormack's office?"

She nodded silently, her eyes moistening.

O'Shea paused for a moment. "Can I get you something to drink?"

She shook her head, and a tear fell on her cheek.

"Mrs. Kunz, would you like to accompany me to your place of residence? I have to pick up your mother."

"My mother! Oh my God," she jumped out of her chair shouting, "You're going to arrest her, too? I thought you were my friend!"

"I'm sorry, Mrs. Kunz. I have a job to do."

CHAPTER 27

1973

If there was a place in the county smaller than Piermont, it was probably Bardonia. One could drive through it in the time it took to sneeze, or so they said. It comprised little more than a bank, a post office, a medical building, and the law offices of Gilbert McCormack, Esq.

Leaning back in his chair, Gil wondered what he could do for the young woman sitting across from him.

"How many policemen came?"

"Two, I think, and Chief O'Shea. Then the ambulance came and took her away. My mother wanted to press charges against her, but the chief said no. Instead, he gave me your card and told me to call you."

"I'll do what I can to help you, but I think it would be a good idea for me to speak with your mother. Do you think you could bring her in tomorrow?"

"Oh sure, but she'll tell you the same thing."

"That's fine. I would just like to have her tell it as she saw it, okay? In the meantime, please don't discuss this matter with anyone. In fact, if the police or anyone else calls you, tell them to call me. Do you understand?"

"Yes, of course."

"Good. Now go home and get a good night's rest."

* * *

The New City courthouse is a two-story stucco building that was erected by immigrants from Ireland in the early 1900s. The walkway from the main street is lined with wooden benches, a popular gathering place on balmy afternoons. Wide marble steps lead to the main entrance, where visitors are greeted, and sometimes frisked, by members of the sheriff's department, who stand guard twenty-four hours a day. The long, narrow corridors that lead to the courtrooms on the second floor are cold and drafty, an effect barely softened by the steamy employee coffee room.

At the first hearing of the morning, two women stood before Judge John Gallucci as Gil McCormack argued that their $10,000 bail was excessive. Alice glared angrily out the large windows overlooking the courtyard below. Kathy, her head bowed, studied the cracks in the wooden floor as McCormack told the judge they were respected members of the community and owned a home in the village.

"It is highly unlikely, Your Honor, that my clients will skip town."

But the judge set bail at $5,000 each and remanded them to the county jail.

Kathy paled at the thought that she and her mother would be thrown in the overcrowded jail. Suddenly, she heard a familiar voice. She turned to see Peter talking to a sheriff deputy in the rear of the courtroom.

"Peter!" she cried out. "Where have you been?" She ran to him and threw her arms around his neck, sobbing. I've been so worried about you."

People stared. Clearly uncomfortable, embarrassed by his wife's outburst, Peter quickly pulled away from her.

"I'm sorry, deputy," he apologized. He walked to the bench and addressed the judge. "Your Honor, I'm Peter Kunz. I've been out of town and I haven't had an opportunity to get to a bank, but I would like to post bail for my wife and mother-in-law. If you will allow me some time, sir, I will return with the bail."

Shocked and humiliated by Peter's public rejection of her, Kathy barely heard the judge place her and her mother in the custody of Chief O'Shea. The slim black hands of the octagonal clock in the chief's office pointed to four ten when Peter returned and handed over the bail money. He asked Alice and Kathy to wait by the front door while he brought the truck around.

It had rained on and off all day, and the rain had turned into a cold, driving storm. The truck pulled up to the curb, Peter leaning over to open the passenger door as mother and daughter, arm in arm, their coat collars turned up around their necks, ran to climb in. The wind blew wildly at their hair; the rain pelted their backs.

No one spoke on the drive home. The only sound was the whoosh, whoosh, whoosh of the howling winds and the slap, slap, slap of the windshield wipers fighting a losing battle against the rain.

Peter pulled into the driveway but made no attempt to get out. Instead, he reached into his jacket pocket, pulled out a bankbook, and handed it to his mother-in-law. "I'm sorry, but I couldn't afford your bail. I went to the bank and explained the problem to the manager, and he let me withdraw the money from your savings account."

Alice opened it and stared at the balance--$2.10-- her lifetime savings wiped out. "It's not even enough to buy a lousy meal!"

* * *

The office buzzer sounded before Gil McCormack had a chance to get very far with his morning coffee and his mail. He pressed the button that brought his secretary on the line. "A Mr. Kunz is here and wishes to speak with you. He says it's urgent."

"Please show him in. This should be interesting."

The man who entered looked older than he had at the arraignment. He was pale and serious; his short, dark hair, neatly combed back from his forehead, emphasized his dark, almost black eyes. His somber suit made him appear even smaller than his five-foot-six frame.

McCormack stood up and shook Peter Kunz's hand. "What can I do for you, Mr. Kunz?" McCormack asked, settling back in his chair.

"It's about my wife," the young man said, "I want to help her."

"Well," McCormack replied. "She certainly could use some help. I'm glad you're here."

"Kathy is a very sick woman," Peter informed him, "I want you to help her."

"I will try," McCormack studied the young man in the chair, wondering what sort of assistance he had in mind.

"First," he went on, "I need some answers. Your wife told me some things about your father, your sister, and ...you. I would like to know how much of what she's told me is the truth."

"Probably all of it. But perhaps it is not the *whole* truth. I spoke to her on the phone yesterday and she told me to stay away from you, but I felt compelled to come and tell you my side of the story. To my mind, Kathy's and her mother's guilt or innocence is not the important question."

191

"Oh? And what is the important question?"

"There's a much more crucial fact to be understood, Mr. McCormack, and that is, I believe that Kathy and I have not loved each other from the beginning. We were very fond of each other and we thought we were in love."

"How old were you when you got married?"

"She was fourteen and I was sixteen when we met, and six months later we were married. But we weren't allowed to find out for ourselves that we weren't really in love, so we kept trying to believe we were."

McCormack could see the man was fighting with his conscience.

"All these years," Peter confessed, "we've both struggled against the truth and hurt ourselves. Now, it's got to stop. We can't take any more punishment. I know Kathy can't. She's already had one nervous breakdown."

McCormack picked up his pencil and began flipping it in the air. He listened intently as Peter continued to repeat what Kathy had already told him about the bizarre ethos with which he was raised, bizarre at least in the eyes of the conventional world.

"Do you believe your wife intended to hurt Miss Belknap?"

Peter looked uncomfortable but did not answer immediately. He studied the clock behind McCormack's chair, watching the second hand move before he finally replied, "I believe that Kathy and her mother planned together to dispose of Penny, but that it was mostly a fantasy that Kathy began to carry out as if it were a game, without realizing where it would lead."

"And your mother-in-law?"

"Well. . . I certainly can understand her feelings of loyalty to her daughter. She'd seen how much torture Kathy was putting herself through with her jealousy, and when she saw Penny sitting there, I believe she felt something decisive had to be done, so she picked up the hammer and struck."

Sweat beads began to surface on his face. Peter removed a white linen handkerchief from his back pocket and wiped his brow. He paused for a moment, looked McCormack in the eye, his voice almost a whisper, "Don't misunderstand me, Mr. McCormack, I can see why Kathy can't admit this: it would put her mother in jail. She wouldn't be able to live

192

with that on her conscience. So, she has to fight in court, and I agree to that. That's why I'm here. I want to pay you to help her. I don't have any money right now, but I promise to pay you monthly. I earn a good living. I want to pay for my mother-in-law, too, because I know she doesn't have any money left. She only did what she had to do because she couldn't bear to see Kathy continue to torture herself."

He listened as the young man sitting before him struggled with his words. It was obvious he was troubled and when he became silent and stood up, he shook the young man's hand in farewell and felt a pang of pity for him. As he left the office, Peter's look of helplessness reminded him of an incident that happened many years ago in the military. He had witnessed the court-martialing of a private for a minor offense: falling asleep while guarding a garbage dump. He remembered the feeling of helplessness he had felt for this young marine and believed that if the boy had adequate legal representation, he would not have been dishonorably discharged from the military. After the war he went to law school and became a lawyer to help the under-dog and make sure justice was served.

* * *

Sharp pains in her lower back awakened Kathy with a start. She sat up in bed slowly; it seemed as if every muscle in her body ached. A feeling of dread crept over her. She folded her arms across her chest, trying to calm herself. She realized she was about to have her first child, alone. The thought frightened her, and she began to cry. She rolled back onto her pillow. Why did Peter abandon her? Did she love him too much? Where did she go wrong? Her thoughts were disrupted by another stab of sharp pain, which seemed to go on forever. She held her breath, waiting for it to subside, holding tightly to the side of the bed. Beads of perspiration began to form on her face. The next contraction doubled her over and she screamed, "Momma, Momma! *Come quick!*"

Alice came running into the room, pulling on a tattered robe, her disheveled hair hanging in her face, her eyes heavy with sleep. "Damn ya, Kathy, yer water's broke. I told ya yesterday ya wuz in labor, but ya never pay no attention to me. After havin' ten kids, I oughta know when I see somebody in labor, dontcha think?"

"Don't lecture me now, Momma, please. Help me out of bed."

"Stay right there, I'm callin' a cab. This kid's in a hurry." Alice ran down the hallway to the kitchen, shouting back to her daughter, "Keep yer legs crossed, Kathy, and fer God's sake don't bear down!"

Less than two hours later, a bedraggled Alice woke up from her doze as Dr. Roth entered the hospital waiting room. He smiled at the elderly women and softly said, "Congratulations, Grandma, your daughter just delivered a beautiful seven-pound girl."

CHAPTER 28

1975

The indictment of Katherine Kunz and Alice Jackson was handed down in late 1974.

Kathy freely admitted having written the notes that Peter had pieced together and turned over to Chief O'Shea as evidence of her intent, but she also consistently maintained that they were written as a release of her mounting tension and anxieties and not for the purpose of planning a murder.

McCormack made a pretrial motion, seeking to suppress the use of the notes as evidence against Kathy. He argued that such use would violate the rule of law governing spousal communications privilege, which dated back to the English common law and under which one spouse could be legally prevented from testifying against the other about confidential communications made during marriage. He contended that Peter was only able to get hold of the notes because, as her husband, he had intimate knowledge of Kathy's habit to put all her thoughts on paper—a habit instilled in her by his own father.

McCormack knew that his application was an effort to stretch the spousal privilege to apply to a situation where a husband would incriminate his wife willingly. He didn't have much hope that Judge Gallucci, who was not an imaginative or innovative jurist, would grant his application, but he had to try. As he anticipated, Judge Gallucci denied his motion, with leave to renew during the trial, and set the trial to begin on March 12, 1975. Peter hadn't been home since the day of the assault, and a part of Kathy had died when he left. She had spent her last months of pregnancy alone, reliving the past and the happy years of marriage. Peter was on her mind day and night. Her weekly sessions with the psychiatrist did little to lift her despair.

The days dragged into weeks, and only the thought of her baby—their baby—kept her afloat. She had convinced herself that Peter would return when the baby was born, but that did not happen. On the day of her discharge from the maternity ward, she sat on the edge of her bed, holding

195

her daughter, waiting for him to come for them. It was Alice who finally called a cab to take them home.

With dread, Alice watched Kathy, in her black dress and loafers, hurry up the marble stairs to the courtroom, her baby cradled in her arms. Alice's concern for her daughter's sanity grew by the day. Kathy had been suffering from insomnia, and on the first day of her trial, the strain of months' worth of sleepless nights clearly showed on her face. She had become disoriented and nervous, unsure of herself, unable to concentrate. Alice feared the stress of the trial would push Kathy over the edge.

Slowed down by a heavy diaper bag loaded with bottles, lollipops, cookies, and raisins, Alice had a hard time keeping up with her daughter as she hurried down the corridors looking for Gil McCormack.

It seemed as if Kathy's motor was running in all directions at once. Her eyes darted from person to person, searching for McCormack. She spotted him in the coffee room.

"I'm sorry," she said in a low, breathless voice. "I had to bring Cara with me. My sister Anna was supposed to take care of her but never showed up."

"That's all right, Kathy, I don't think the judge will mind—provided, of course, you keep her quiet."

"Don't worry, Mr. McCormack," Alice assured him, "she ain't gonna cry, not wit all the stuff I got in this here bag. I know how to keep a kid quiet. I had ten of 'em!"

"Will Peter be here today? "Kathy asked. Her voice trembled with anxiety.

"I'm sure he'll be somewhere in the courthouse today, Kathy, but he won't be allowed in the courtroom."

"Why not?"

"Because he's going to be a witness at the trial and witnesses are not allowed into the courtroom before they testify."

Kathy's face crumpled. She had wanted him there, wanted him to see his daughter, had hoped he would be at her side.

"Kathy—" McCormack's voice was gentle. "Have you given any consideration to our discussion of yesterday? You still have time to change your mind, you know."

Afraid to let her tears escape, Kathy didn't look up at him and only shook her head. Sensing McCormack's need to talk to her in private, Alice took Baby Cara and began to pace the hallways.

"Kathy, listen to me," McCormack continued. "I want to make sure you understand the deal. If you plead guilty to simple assault—do you understand what that means, Kathy? *Simple assault.*" He pronounced the words slowly and deliberately.

She nodded, still staring at the floor.

"The judge has promised probation. No jail. Do you understand me, Kathy? *No jail.*"

She lifted her head to meet his eyes. The look on her face was frightening, almost menacing. "Mr. McCormack," she began slowly and defiantly, "I've told you before and I'll tell you again: I am not guilty of anything but protecting my mother. I will not plead guilty to anything else, even if they send me to jail. I am not guilty, do you understand?" Her voice was loud. "I am not guilty!" She covered her face with her hands and started to sob.

McCormack saw his wife hurrying up the stairs and called to her. "Tess, I'm glad you're here. Please take Mrs. Kunz to the ladies' room and help her pull herself together. I don't want the jurors to see her this way."

It was almost ten o'clock when sheriff's deputy emerged from the courtroom.

"Everyone in the courtroom. The court is now in session."

Alice, who until then sat quietly on a wooden bench, swiftly rose, lifted the baby to her shoulder, and rushed to the ladies' room. "Hurry up, Kathy, it's time to go."

Hugging Baby Cara tightly to her chest, Kathy approached the courtroom door.

The deputy stopped her. "I'm sorry, miss, babies are not allowed in the courtroom. You'll have to wait outside."

"That's fine with me," Kathy replied, a faint smile on her lips.

Tess stepped forward. "These are Mrs. Kunz and Mrs. Jackson, the defendants in this trial."

"I don't care who they are," the deputy retorted, "babies are not allowed in the courtroom."

The women exchanged glances as the deputy blocked their path.

197

"Wait here," Tess said. "I'll be right back." She walked to the defense table and whispered into her husband's ear. McCormack quickly made his way out of the courtroom.

He smiled at the deputy, whom he had known for many years. "Helen, would you please allow my clients to enter? I don't think the judge will mind this beautiful child in the courtroom, do you?"

"Mr. . . . Mr. McCormack," the deputy stuttered nervously, "you know the rules better than me. You know I can't allow this baby in the courtroom."

McCormack smiled again, his grin amiable. "In that case, perhaps the county will provide a babysitter for Mrs. Kunz?"

"I've got to talk to the judge. Please wait here. I'll be right back." The deputy scurried down the hallway into the judge's chambers.

McCormack watched her go with a knowing smile. Of course, he knew the rules, but he had wanted the jury to see Kathy's child. The confrontation with the deputy and his suggestion of a county-paid babysitter had all but ensured that. As he looked at the baby in Kathy's arms, he thought how ironic it was that she should look so much like her father. Her large, dark, olive-shaped eyes overpowered her otherwise tiny features. Fine, silky dark hair framed her face.

The judge called McCormack to his chambers.

"Mr. McCormack, you know I can't allow children in my courtroom."

"I'm sorry, Your Honor, but you wouldn't want that poor baby left unattended out in the hallway, when both of her caregivers must be present in the courtroom, would you?"

"I'll give you one hour to find a babysitter," the judge said, showing signs of impatience. "I don't have time to play games, I have a court to run. Tell Helen to get on the phone. Maybe one of Mrs. Kunz's sisters can come down here."

Meanwhile, Baby Cara was the center of attention. Fresh from her nap, she toddled up and down the hallways, smiling an almost-toothless smile, leaving a trail of cookie crumbs and raisins. She was still unsteady on her feet and walked like a tiny adorable drunken sailor.

Close to eleven o'clock, McCormack reappeared and spoke to his wife. "I think you'll have to take care of Cara for a while. We haven't

198

been able to find a sitter and I don't want to start the case with a hostile judge."

Helen shouted from the courtroom door, "Everyone in the courtroom. Court is now in session."

Kathy's face turned ashen. The moment she had been dreading had arrived.

CHAPTER 29

1975

It had taken three days to select a jury of six men and six women—two retirees, a farmer's wife, two schoolteachers, a construction worker, two housewives, a nurse, a phone company repairman, a salesman, and a florist.

The courtroom was filled to capacity. As Gil McCormack and the defendants entered and took their seats, all eyes were on them, faint whispers rustling among the rows of spectators.

Directly behind the witness chair, almost hidden, was a narrow door. Helen the deputy stood before it, her hand resting on the doorknob. When everyone was seated, she opened it, announcing: "Please rise. County court is now in session, the Honorable John Gallucci presiding."

McCormack had tried many cases before Judge Gallucci and knew him to be a fair though conservative judge, a devout Catholic and a devoted family man, the father of two daughters and a son. McCormack wondered what his reaction would be when he heard about the way Kathy had been treated in her in-laws' household.

The courtroom became silent as the judge entered the room and quickly directed the prosecuting attorney to begin his opening statement.

Peter Branti, the prosecutor, dressed immaculately in a blue pinstriped suit, rose slowly and approached the wooden railing in front of the jury box. All eyes followed him. A former truck driver in his early thirties, he had studied law at night and had already earned a reputation for his self-confidence in the three years he had been an assistant district attorney. "A trial, ladies and gentlemen of the jury, is nothing more than a search for the truth. In my opinion, this is a simple case, because there are only two basic issues—did the defendants attempt to cause the death of Penny Belknap, and did they, in fact, cause the injury."

With a great deal of repetition and backtracking, Mr. Branti gave his account of the assault and the events leading up to it. He discussed Kathy's notes at length. "Mr. McCormack will tell you these are a scorned woman's innermost thoughts. I say, it's a diary of death. It gives us the bait that was used to lure the victim into the den of depravity. It gives us the very clothes that were worn in the commission of the crime. How many times have you heard the expression 'she was dressed to kill?' When I read these notes," he paused for a moment, looked at the jurors and smiled, "it took on a new meaning for me."

As he continued to speak, Branti looked each juror in the eye, one by one, emphasizing the dramatic steps of the alleged murder plot. He began with Kathy digging a grave in her backyard; renting a car; moving on to her luring Penny back to her home so that she could carry out her nefarious plans.

"In conclusion," a broad smile lit up Branti's handsome face, "I will prove that Katherine Kunz and Alice Jackson planned together to kill Penny Belknap. I want you to listen carefully to the evidence and not be blinded by the smoke screens, the red herrings, the non-issues. Remember, we are here to search out the truth."

He thanked the jurors for their attention, turned, nodded courteously to McCormack, and returned to his table, content with his presentation. He had made it sound simple but damning.

The courtroom fell silent, the audience absorbing the impact of his words, studying the expressions on the jurors' faces.

*   *   *

Gil McCormack's reputation among his colleagues was that of a lawyer's lawyer—a hard but clean fighter, intimidating but sophisticated. Carefully, he arranged his yellow lined pages on the desk in front of the jury box.

He knew the district attorney's office had a strong evidential case against the defendants. His plan was to overwhelm the jurors with the brute force of Kathy's life story. Determined but apprehensive, he stood up and faced the jury. He didn't know how far Judge Gallucci would allow him to go in describing Kathy's background, which, without a plea of temporary insanity, could be considered immaterial.

"Ladies and gentlemen of the jury, I do not believe *any* case is simple, nor do I believe any case can be decided in a vacuum. There will be testimony offered to you that Alice Jackson had ten children. You will hear about the hardships she endured in raising these children alone."

Bitter, Alice barely listened. Her degree of hostility and defensiveness, her sarcasm and anger, had intensified a great deal since the indictment. The whole trial, as far as she was concerned, was a ridiculous mistake.

She turned away from McCormack and focused on the familiar sounds of ball playing in the courtyard, drifting into the open window of the courtroom. How many years had she sat alongside various courtyards, watching her kids play ball? Her kids were grown now. She had done her best.

Suddenly, McCormack's words got her attention. The expression on Alice's face slowly changed from boredom to disbelief and finally to outrage as she listened to his words: "And we will offer evidence as to what Oskar Kunz did when he learned that his fifteen-year-old daughter-in-law was pregnant." From time to time, Alice looked at Kathy but her daughter, sitting motionless with a fixed blank stare, ignored her. At the end of McCormack's opening statement, Alice was visibly shaken. She had no idea that Kathy had ever been pregnant before.

CHAPTER 30

1975

At the courthouse entrance, there was a line to get through security. The courthouse buzzed with activity: murder trials were an uncommon occurrence in the little town. For the most part, Kathy felt like an uninvolved observer at someone else's ordeal, but when she heard Penny Belknap called to the witness stand, she sat up and listened.

When Penny walked into the courtroom, the room fell silent. She walked directly to the witness box, without looking at the defense table. When Kathy raised her face to look at Penny, she saw that Penny had cropped her long hair to her shoulders and parted it in the middle. Her printed dirndl skirt hung almost to her socks and loafers, making her appear shorter and heavier than Kathy remembered. *Perhaps,* she thought, *it was because I was so pregnant that I thought she looked so thin.*

Peter Branti walked up to the witness box and smiled.

"Please state your name and address."

"My name is Penny Belknap and I live at 455 Main Street, Boston, Mass."

"Are you employed?"

"Yes."

"By whom?"

"I'm self-employed, but I usually work for Peter Kunz & Co."

"How long have you known Peter Kunz?"

"Since the end of June or first week of July 1973."

"Will you tell us where you first met Mr. Kunz?"

"I was a wardrobe mistress at Nation TV Studio in Boston, Mass. He came to do a job at the studio."

"What was the nature of your relationship with him at that time?" Penny leaned forward in her chair and for the moment pondered her answer. Her mouth twitched and then she looked away. "That's when we got romantically involved."

"Did you know if Mr. Kunz was married?"

"Yes, I did," she replied. "Peter told me."

"Did Mrs. Kunz know of this relationship?"

"Yes, Peter had told me she did. Then Kathy told me."

"Did you ever take a trip with Mr. Kunz?"

"Yes, I did."

"Where did you go?"

"Haiti."

"Did Mrs. Kunz know of the trip?"

"I found out on October 23, 1973, that she knew."

"Have you ever met Mrs. Kunz?"

"Yes, on October 23."

"Had you ever spoken to Mrs. Kunz prior to October 1973?"

"No."

"Do you see Mrs. Kunz in this courtroom?"

"Yes, I do."

"Will you stand and point her out?"

The witness stood up. For a moment, the two women's eyes met. Penny pointed a finger at the defendant and sat down. Kathy looked away as if in a daze.

Branti waited a moment then asked, "Do you know an individual named Alice Jackson?"

"Yes, I do."

"Do you see her here?"

"Yes, I do."

"Please stand and point her out."

Alice, who had again been gazing out the window, turned her cold eyes on the witness. Penny pointed to Alice but could not avoid her unmistakable look of hostility.

"Had you ever spoken with Mrs. Jackson prior to October23?"

"No, I had not."

"When did you first meet the defendant, Katherine Kunz?"

"On the morning of October 23, in front of my apartment, at about ten minutes past eight. I was on my way to work when a car pulled up beside me, and that's when I first saw her."

"How was she attired?"

"She wore a black wig and sunglasses."

"Did she identify herself to you?"

"Not immediately. Then, she said, 'Do you know who I am?' I looked at her and said, 'Maybe if you take off your dark glasses.' And she said, 'I'm Peter's wife, Kathy, and I think we should have a talk.' And I said, 'I think so, too.' I wasn't too surprised because Peter had told me all about her. He had also suggested we meet and get to know each other. Then she offered me a ride to work."

Branti continued with his questions: "As best as you can remember, what did you say to her and what did the defendant say to you"

"We talked about many things, and I don't remember what happened exactly at what point, but she said she knew about me, and we talked about the things Peter had told me about her—I mean, knew about us—and then she told me that she felt I was one of many to come. Then she said, 'I think I'd better tell you Peter has had a serious accident at work and he is in the Rivervale Hospital in Ohio.' She suggested we go to Ohio to surprise Peter. Since I knew he wanted us to meet, I thought this was a fun idea and agreed to go with her."

"Did the defendant drive you to work at that time?"

"No, she did not."

"Did you drive some other place?"

"Yes, we did."

"Where was that?"

"To the Kunz home in Piermont, New York."

"Who suggested the drive to Piermont?"

"Kathy because she said she needed to pick up a check and then we could take a shuttle to Ohio."

"Did you come of your own free will at that time?"

"Yes, I did."

"Did you continue to discuss your relationship with Mr. Kunz on the way down, in the car?"

"Yes, we did."

"Was this trip a nonstop trip?"

"No, it was not. I asked if I could call my boss and we stopped at a place on the road and used the pay phone to call my office."

"After you made the phone call, what happened?"

"Well, Kathy pulled the car around the back of the garage and went into the ladies' room. I got her a cup of coffee and she said she had a couple of thermoses in the back of the car if I wanted any juice. One of them had vitamins in it, she said. And I said, 'No, I don't drink when I travel'."

"Did you stop at any other place along the way?"

"Yes. We stopped at approximately four places, all told: three gas stations and a lookout point on the Palisades Parkway, a resting spot. We stretched our legs and just sort of walked around a little at the lookout."

"Did you ever drink any of the juice that was in either thermos?"

"No."

"Did Mrs. Kunz ever offer it to you again?"

"In the house, she offered me juice."

Through a series of questions, Branti encouraged Penny to tell the jury that she was brought to Piermont at approximately two thirty in the afternoon and that Mrs. Jackson was the only other person in the house. She recounted that when they got into the house, Kathy said she would call the doctor to find out how Peter was doing. She said the kitchen phone wasn't working so Kathy went downstairs to the playroom to use an extension. Penny further testified that when Kathy came back, she was informed that she wouldn't be able to go and see Peter, because she wasn't a family member. Penny testified that Kathy left the house about three o'clock in the afternoon but when she returned, Penny was told that she *could* see Peter in the morning.

Branti continued, "Where did you have dinner that evening?"

"Sitting around the counter in the kitchen of the house."

"Did you have anything to drink with your meal?"

"Yes. I asked for juice and was told to help myself to the thermos in the refrigerator. I took a sip of the drink but spit it out because it was bitter. Then I took a bottle of soda that was in the icebox."

"Were you invited to spend the night there?"

"Yes, I was."

"Did you stay of your own free will?"

"Yes, I did."

"Did anything unusual occur during the night?"

"I went to bed around eleven o'clock, and later that night, I heard the phone ring and so it sort of woke me up. And then later on, I woke up and Kathy was in the room. She was getting something out of her mother's closet, and she said, 'Don't worry, go back to sleep. I'm just getting something out of the closet.' So, I went back to sleep."

"Would you tell the jury what happened in the morning? Did you have breakfast?"

"I asked again for a glass of juice."

"Did you drink that juice?"

"No. There was a glass in the refrigerator, but it tasted like it came from the thermos, so I threw it out and washed the glass."

"Miss Belknap, will you tell the court why you didn't go to Ohio in the morning?"

"First, because Kathy started getting sick and throwing up and also because she was looking for some check she said she needed to cash."

"What were you doing while Mrs. Kunz was throwing up?"

"I was watching television and pacing back and forth along the hallway, looking at pictures and the cactus on the windowsill. Then I decided I just had to sit down and wait it out, because if she was sick, I couldn't rush it."

"Now, while you were waiting it out-- as you put it-- what, if anything, happened?"

"Well, I was sitting watching television and around ten minutes after eleven, I felt a sharp blow on the back of my head. I had long hair to the middle of my back, and it was pinned up under a headscarf, which probably saved my life. When I was hit on the head, I fell forward and started to black out."

"Did you black out at that time?"

"No, I did not. I jumped up, moved forward about four or five steps, and turned back and saw Mrs. Jackson standing there with a hammer in her hand. Just standing there! I screamed out, 'Crazy old woman!' and turned to find Kathy—she was behind me to my left, heading toward the kitchen. I said, 'So this is it,' and Kathy said, 'Yes, this is it.' Then I ran toward the front door, opened the screen door, and Kathy said, 'Don't bother, it's locked!' I turned away from the door and Mrs. Jackson hit me in the nose with the hammer. I started to scream, and I turned back to the door and threw myself against the screen and knocked it out, but I couldn't get myself over it, and they were both hitting me on the head. So, I turned back and saw Kathy and grabbed at her hair, but I only pulled her wig off."

"Did Kathy have anything in her hand at that time?"

"She had a square frying pan in her hand. Then, I ran to the back door. Kathy ran around one side of the dining-room table and I ran around the other. Her mother was to my right and coming up behind me.

"Then, Kathy and I had a rather bizarre conversation: 'No, don't open that door.' 'Yes, I will.' 'No, you won't.' I struggled and got to the door and pulled it back, but I couldn't get it all the way open. I went down on my knees and had one knee on one side of the sliding door and one knee on the other. My arms were trying to protect my head, and I was screaming the whole time, 'Police! Police! Someone help me!'

"They continued pulling my hair and all I could hear was Kathy yelling, 'Shut up you little bitch.'

"Then I couldn't hold on anymore because they kept pulling me back with my sweater. The next thing I remember is being inside the door on my knees. Kathy was holding my head down and her mother was hitting me, so I bit Kathy on the arm as hard as I could. She screamed and let go of me. I got up and somehow got to the middle of the room, and I thought maybe if I pretended to pass out, they would stop hitting me."

"What happened next?" Branti's voice was filled with sympathy.

"I was sitting on the floor and Kathy was standing over me with the frying pan in her hand, and then there was a pounding on the door. Kathy went to open it, and a man was there. She yelled at him to 'mind his own business' and slammed the door in his face!

"Then, her mother started swinging at me again. This time I was able to grab the hammer, but I couldn't get it away from her. For an old lady she was pretty strong. Then, there was another pounding on the door and Kathy went to the door again and tried to close it. I screamed, 'No! No! HELP ME!' Somehow, I managed to get to the man in the doorway, and I hung onto his knees. I wouldn't let go till the police came."

The jurors listened intently. Branti walked back to his table and checked his notes.

Kathy had not moved her eyes from Penny, staring, almost unseeing.

McCormack sat quietly, flipping his pencil.

The only one who appeared to pay no attention was Alice. Her eyes were fixed on the window, daydreaming.

Branti moved to the witness box. "Miss Belknap, I have one last question. While they were taking you out of the house, did you hear anyone say anything?"

"The only thing I remember was Kathy shouting, "Look at that! She's got blood all over my floor! She should have to clean it up!"

Branti looked up at the Judge: "I have no further questions at this time, Your Honor."

CHAPTER 31

1975

Gil McCormack rose from the defense table and buttoned his jacket. He walked to the witness and smiled. "Miss Belknap, would you do me a favor and keep your voice up so that all the jurors can hear your answers?"

She nodded and appeared confident.

"I understand from your testimony that your address is in Boston, Mass."

The witness nodded again.

"The reason I ask is that when Mr. Branti read the addresses of the potential witnesses, he gave your legal address as Dumont, New Jersey. Have you ever lived in New Jersey?"

"I do now."

"Where does Peter Kunz live?"

"His legal address is in Piermont, New York."

McCormack's eyebrows raised in mock surprise. "His *legal* address? Where does he live now?"

"With me, in Tenafly."

"How long has his legal address been in Piermont?"

"Since August 1972."

"You say you first met Mr. Kunz the end of June or first week of July 1973?"

"Yes."

"When did you get romantically involved with Peter Kunz?"

"It would have been the first part of July, 1973."

"Did you have an apartment or a home?"

"An apartment."

"And who did you live with?"

"With two roommates."

"Male or female roommates?"

"Two men."

McCormack's voice deepened, "And, how long did you live with two men?"

Branti jumped to his feet, his face flushed with anger. "Your Honor, I object! It's immaterial and irrelevant!"

Judge Gallucci replied calmly, "I'll take it on the question of credibility." He turned to the witness. "Please answer the question."

"About a year," Penny replied, seemingly unfazed by the clashing of the attorneys.

McCormack walked back to the defense table and checked his notes, letting the words of the exchange linger in the air. When he walked back to the witness he asked, "And where did you live before that?"

Branti was on his feet again. "Your Honor, irrelevant!"

"Yes," the judge agreed, "I think it's immaterial as to where she lived before that. We can go back to when she was two years old, if we keep this up."

"Your Honor," McCormack's voice was mild, "I have no intention of going back to when the witness was two years old. But, subject to connection, I intend to show that this is relevant."

In an angry tone, the Judge said, "Approach the bench, please."

The lawyers walked to the side of the judge's bench. The courtroom silence was deafening as the three men whispered among themselves. The Judge lifted his head and said, "You may continue, Mr. McCormack."

McCormack walked back to the defense table, picked up his pen and began flipping it. When he walked back to the witness, he smiled. "Miss Belknap, did you ever live in Colorado?"

"Yes, I worked there."

"Where were you employed?"

"In a bar-restaurant and another place. . ."

Branti jumped to his feet to prevent her from finishing her sentence. "That's immaterial your Honor."

"I'm going to take this on the credibility of the witness and for no other purpose. If I feel there is no connection, I will instruct the jury to disregard it."

The witness finished her answer, "The other place I worked, I got fired. I heard rumors afterwards that it was a house of ill repute."

McCormack raised his eyebrows and repeated her words in a questioning voice: "A house of prostitution?"

Penny smiled. Seemingly comfortable with her answer. "Yes, that's what I heard."

"When you first met Peter Kunz, were you engaged to either of the men you were living with?"

"Engaged? No, but I had contemplated marrying one of them."

"I believe you testified that you met Peter Kunz in late June and that you went to Haiti with him in July of that year. Is that correct?"

"Actually, he went first. I flew down later."

"And you lived with him for six weeks in Haiti?"

"Yes."

"Were you employed by your lover?"

Branti was on his feet again. His voice was loud and pleading, "Your Honor, I Object to the form of the question."

Judge Gallucci took off his glasses and rubbed his eyes. He paused a moment then looked down at the court stenographer: "Yes, strike the word *lover*." He turned to look at the jury. "Disregard the word *lover*."

McCormack leaned toward the witness, his voice in a mocking whisper said: "Well. . . may I just put this a different way: Miss Belknap, did you say you were romantically involved with Peter Kunz?"

"Yes."

"And you spent some time with him in Haiti?"

"Yes."

"I apologize if I have offended your sensibilities by using the term 'lover.' I'm sorry. I presume I have offended Mr. Branti's." There was a laughter in the courtroom. The Judge banged his gavel for silence. Then he addressed the jurors: "Please strike these remarks. The jury will disregard them. They are not evidence in this case." He was not smiling but some of the jurors were.

McCormack continued. "I apologize your Honor." He walked back to the defense table and took a moment to look at his notes. When he returned to the witness, he asked, "When you first met Peter Kunz in June or July 1973, did you know where he lived?"

"Yes, Piermont."

"You knew the address?"

"Yes, Peter told me where he lived."

"Did you communicate with him after his return from Haiti?"

"Yes, through letters."

"At that address?"

"No, not at that address."

"Where did you send your letters?"

"To his parents' house."

"If I correctly understood your testimony on direct examination, you stated that Peter Kunz said his wife knew about your relationship and condoned it. Yet the letters you wrote to him were sent in care of his parents?"

"Yes, that's what Peter wanted."

"Miss Belknap, had you ever seen Mrs. Kunz before October 23, 1973?"

"No."

"Had you ever seen any pictures of her?"

"Yes, I saw pictures in Peter's portfolio."

"Photographs and drawings?"

"Yes."

"Do you have any distinct recollection of seeing a drawing he had done of his wife prior to October . . .uh . . .?"

"I remember seeing one of her sleeping, but I wouldn't have recognized her."

"By the way, did Peter Kunz, at any time, when you first met him or during your stay in Haiti, make any drawings of you?"

"Yes." She smiled remembering.

"Were they full-figure drawings?"

"Yes."

"Clothed or unclothed?"

"One was unclothed."

"And were they in the same artist's scrapbook in which you saw pictures of his sleeping wife?"

"If that was her, yes."

"In other words, you saw a photograph of her nude?"

"It was not a photograph. It was a drawing."

Branti's head jerked, his face red with anger, his words pleading: "Your Honor, your Honor, I'm going to object to any further questions. He's badgering the witness."

213

"As I said before Mr. Branti, I'm taking it on the credibility of the witness and for no other purpose." Branti's expression was easy to read.

McCormack produced a series of photographs and showed them to the witness, asking her to identify each one. Without any hostility or rancor, Penny patiently scanned each and told him that most of them were taken in Haiti, some with clothes and some without.

McCormack addressed the Judge: "Your Honor, may I show these pictures to the jury?"

Branti was again annoyed: "Your Honor, they have not been offered in evidence!"

McCormack turned to the prosecutor, a mirthless smile on his face. "My apologies, Mr. Branti. Your Honor, may I offer them into evidence?"

Before the Judge could answer, Branti offered, "Your Honor, they are very nice photographs. However, I object to them being admitted into evidence on the grounds that they are immaterial and irrelevant!"

"Overruled. I will admit them solely on the believability of the witness."

Branti quickly walked up to the judge's bench. "Your Honor, may we have a conference?"

"You can come to the side bar and I will talk to you."

The judge turned to the jurors. "Ladies and gentlemen, with respect to the conference, it usually means it is a question of law that I will have to decide on. It is no concern of yours. Do not speculate or guess as to what is discussed."

The conference was brief. Addressing the court clerk, the judge said, "The pictures will be admitted into evidence with an exception." He turned to McCormack. "Did you want to show them to the jury?"

"Thank you, Your Honor, I have a few more questions." McCormack turned back to the witness. "This sketch that Mr. Kunz drew of you in the nude, where was that drawn?"

"Haiti."

"And, to the best of your recollection, was that kept in the sketchbook with the pictures of his wife?"

"Yes."

"Miss Belknap, during your trip to Piermont, did you discuss with Mrs. Kunz the fact that you had worked in a house of prostitution in Colorado?"

"Objection, Your Honor."

"Overruled."

Penny smiled. "That's just my little joke. I don't really know it for a fact."

"As a joke?" McCormack repeated, "Or, at least your own private joke. Did you tell Mrs. Kunz that you had worked in a house of prostitution?"

"Yes, as a matter of fact I did tell her that but, as I've said before, I really didn't know for sure."

"And did you tell her that your relationship with Mr. Kunz wasn't very important to you, that he was just another friend-- a friend that kept your juices flowing?"

She laughed, "Yes." She lowered her eyes but seemed to enjoy hearing her own words.

"And did you also tell her that you had planned on marrying one of the men you lived with until an accident left him a paraplegic?"

"No."

"Had he been your lover before the accident?"

"Yes."

"Objection."

"Overruled."

"And did you discuss with Mrs. Kunz that you had had a baby and that you had given it up for adoption?"

She quickly answered, "Yes, but..."

"Your Honor!" Branti shouted as he jumped out of his seat.

Judge Gallucci grumbled, "Let it stand. She's already answered it."

"Your Honor," McCormack paused looking up to the Judge, "Your Honor, "I...I didn't hear the answer."

The Judge looked down at the defense attorney, obviously irritated. "She said, 'Yes'. . . Mr. McCormack! I am not going to let you go on and on. I only permitted it on the grounds of credibility, but it has basically no relevance to what occurred on October 24, 1973."

"Yes, Your Honor."

McCormack turned his attention back to the witness. His voice was so loud, her head jerked back. "Now, Mrs. Kunz...excuse me . . ." he lowered his voice. "Miss Belknap, you have testified you wrote Peter Kunz letters, which were addressed to his parents' house. Did Mr. Kunz respond to your letters?"

"Yes, we wrote back and forth."

"When you returned from Haiti, did Mr. Kunz visit you regularly on weekends?"

She smiled. "Yes, every other weekend."

"And when he came to visit you, did he stay in the same apartment as you and the two men?"

"Yes, he did."

"Did you have relations with him on those occasions?"

The question confused her, and she asked, "With Peter? Yes."

Branti's head jerked up as he shouted, "Objection your Honor!"

"Overruled. She's already answered it."

"Did you have. . ." McCormack began again.

"She already answered yes!" The Judge replied in an angry voice.

"I'm sorry Your Honor, I didn't hear the answer."

Addressing the court stenographer, the Judge said, "Please read the answer back."

As McCormack continued his cross-examination, the court clerk handed the Judge a note. He read it and looked at the clock. "Mr. McCormack, will you finish your examination today?"

"No, your Honor."

The Judge turned and addressed the jury. "Due to the lateness of the hour and a personal matter, I will adjourn court until 9 am tomorrow morning."

* * *

Despite her brightly colored dress, Penny Belknap looked pale when court resumed the next morning. McCormack took her through another series of questions leading up to the morning of the assault.

"On the morning of October 24, in the home of Peter Kunz, did you have any breakfast?"

"No."

216

"Nothing?"

"I never eat breakfast."

"Never?" He repeated as if in disbelief.

"But I did this morning, and I threw it up."

He took a moment and looked at her. "Oh, I'm sorry to hear that. How are you feeling now?"

"Fine," she replied quickly.

"Happy to hear that." The attorney's voice full of mock joy. "By the way Miss Belknap, how did you get here today?"

"Peter drove me."

The prosecutor jumped to his feet. "Objection, your Honor!"

"Overruled. You may proceed."

"Miss Belknap, I would like to take you back to the morning of October 24, 1973. Were you getting angry because Mrs. Kunz was sick and because she was looking for a check?"

"Yes, I was getting very restless and very irritated."

"Very what?" He repeats.

"Irritated."

"And… were you becoming angry?"

"Angry at the situation, yes."

"How many times would you say you were hit in the face with the frying pan?"

"I don't know," she said sarcastically, "I wasn't counting."

"You don't have any visible scars on your face, do you?"

"No, No," she said angrily. "I fended them off. She hit *at* my face, not hit my face."

"Perhaps you didn't understand the question, Mrs. Kunz . . . sorry, Mrs. Belknap. I asked if you have any visible scars on your face at this time."

"No, I do not."

Branti was again on his feet. "Your Honor, I believe this witness's name is Penny Belknap, not Mrs. Kunz."

"I'm so sorry. Did I misspeak, Mr. Branti? I apologize, Miss Belknap." McCormack walked back to his desk and picked up some documents.

"I'm going to show you some letters and ask you to look at the salutation and at the signature. Tell me if you recognize the signature."

"Yes, I do."

"Are these letters you wrote to Peter Kunz, husband of Kathy Kunz?"

"I presume so."

"Are they dated?"

"Yes, most of them are from September 1973."

"At this time, your Honor," McCormack waved a stack of letters in the direction of the jurors, "the defense would like to enter these letters into evidence."

"I object, Your Honor!"

"I will sustain the objection unless Mr. McCormack can explain for the record what makes them admissible." The judge looked at the letters. "I don't see any relevance to them at all. They do not contradict anything the witness has testified so far."

"I assure the court, I have every intention of proving clearly and succinctly the materiality of these documents. I am confident the evidence will show they are material. Certainly, I do not believe it is incumbent upon me to reveal my entire defense at this time, Your Honor, but I believe the court has the discretion to accept them subject to connection."

Branti's face turned a bright shade of red as he presented his objection. "This has nothing to do with the credibility of the witness! There is no specific immoral or vicious act, nothing to do with the truth and veracity of this witness, and immaterial to the reason we are in this courtroom today!"

"I will sustain the objection," the judge said. "The witness has admitted to a relationship with Peter Kunz. There are many things in those letters that are irrelevant and immaterial."

"Objection sustained!"

"Your Honor, may I respectfully suggest one thing in response to Mr. Branti's objection? There is nothing there that attacks credibility, even as loose as the morals of modern society may purport to be. But I certainly agree that it goes to the credibility of someone who openly admits to adultery. I further submit, Your Honor, that one of those letters refers to having a baby with Peter Kunz."

The Judge agreed and allowed him to continue with his questioning: "You can ask her about that, but I'm going to rule insofar as the letters are concerned. You've made your argument. I sustain the objection at this time."

McCormack looked relieved. "You Honor, may we have a short recess?"

"We already had one." He replied, "But, I will give you a few minutes."

*   *   *

McCormack continued after the recess. "Mrs. Kunz, did you have a discussion with Peter Kunz about having 'our baby'?"

"My name is Penny Belknap."

"My apologies. Miss Belknap, did you, in fact, have a discussion about having a baby together?"

"We talked about a baby, yes."

"And the baby you were referring to, was it a baby with Mr. Kunz?"

"Yes. Can I tell you what happened?"

"You weren't pregnant, were you?"

"What happened was," she began, "Peter had found out that Kathy was pregnant, and in a moment of passion, and only because of the confusion in his head, he said something about how he wanted me to have his baby, too. If the jury could read the letter, they would see that I said it was the wrong time to ask.

"I also said, 'Don't judge Kathy by what she's going through with her pregnancy. You'll see a lot of changes.' I said I didn't want to talk about a baby because our relationship hadn't gotten to that point yet." Penny seemed satisfied with her explanation.

McCormack smiled at her. "Do you agree the jury should read that letter?" He turned to the judge. "I offer it into evidence."

The Judge replied sternly, "The court makes the rulings with respect to that."

"I renew my objection, Your Honor." Branti quickly put in.

"The court will abide by its prior ruling and sustain the objection."

219

"My objection is simple," Branti said glaring at McCormack. "I submit that it is irrelevant and immaterial to what happened on the 24th of October."

"I've made my ruling," the judge reminded them. He turned to the jury, "Ladies and gentlemen, from time to time, you may hear comments made by me and counsel. I want you to remember they are not part of the evidence in this case. You are to completely disregard them in deciding the case."

"You may continue, Mr. McCormack."

The lawyer cleared his throat and approached the witness box. "On October 23, when Mrs. Kunz picked you up, how was she attired?"

"She was wearing a dark wig, dark glasses, gloves, a red sweater jacket, black turtleneck, black pants, and Peter's socks."

"I'm sorry. I didn't hear that last part."

"Peter's socks." She smiled as if she found this amusing. "She told me she was wearing Peter's socks."

"You testified that on the trip down to Piermont, you discussed the fact that she had had sexual relations with her father-in-law."

"Yes."

"Had you known from other sources that she had sex with her father-in-law?"

"Yes. Peter told me."

McCormack raised his voice when he directed this question to the witness.

"Did Mrs. Kunz tell you that her husband condoned her intimate relationship with his father?"

"Well," she hesitated for a moment, "Yes, she said he knew about it. Yes, he condoned it."

"Would you please tell the court what she told you with respect to it?"

"Well, regarding the seven-year affair with her father-in-law, she told me she did it to keep peace between Peter and his father but that she didn't enjoy it."

McCormack looked up at the Judge: "Your Honor, I have no further questions."

CHAPTER 32

1975

Pale and drawn, Kathy climbed up the marble steps to the courtroom. She hadn't slept all night, apprehensive about seeing Peter, who was scheduled to be the first witness of the day.

But as exhausted as she was, when he walked into the courtroom, her eyes opened wide and her heart began to pound when she saw him. She wanted to cry out, to tell him this was only a nightmare from which they would both wake up—yet deep down, she knew better. As he passed the defense table, she stared at him, repressing the desire to reach out and touch him. In an almost hypnotic trance, she watched him step into the witness box. The court clerk asked him to raise his right hand and place his left hand on the Bible.

"That is unnecessary," Peter stated. "I was raised to be honest." The startled clerk glanced at the judge.

"Mr. Kunz," the judge said, "if you do not wish to be sworn in, you may affirm your testimony. Is that your desire?"

"Yes, Your Honor."

The clerk put down the Bible. "Mr. Kunz, do you affirm to tell the truth, the whole truth, and nothing but the truth?"

"Yes."

The prosecutor rose.

Despite a steady stream of Gil McCormack's objections, Peter recounted how after receiving a phone call from the Piermont chief of police, he took the first flight from Cleveland to New York, rented a car, and drove to the hospital in Nyack to see Penny.

He visited with Penny for several hours before going to the police station to see the chief. At approximately ten p.m. he arrived home where he spoke briefly with his wife, demanding to know why she had brought Penny to their home without his knowledge.

He acknowledged that later that evening, he searched for his wife's notes. When he didn't find what he wanted in the upstairs wastepaper baskets, he went into the garage and searched the large garbage bins. He testified that he stuffed his pockets with all the scraps of notepad paper he could find because he knew his wife always wrote notes to herself and kept them at her bedside.

He left his home at approximately four o'clock the next morning and drove back to Ohio. There he spent hours putting the pieces of the puzzle together.

Branti asked, "Describe what was written on the notes."

"Handwriting in red ink," replied Peter.

"And whose handwriting did you recognize it to be?"

McCormack swiftly rose to his feet. "Your Honor, I just want the record to clearly reflect my objection to any testimony concerning these notes, on the grounds that any notes that a husband has procured allegedly written by his wife—especially his wife of fourteen years—are confidential communications, and certainly the law of the state of New York recognizes fully that it's improper for confidential communications to be offered into evidence."

"I will reserve decision with respect to it at this time, Mr. McCormack," Judge Gallucci responded. "Answer the question, Mr. Kunz."

"My wife's handwriting."

"Have you ever seen your wife's handwriting before?"

"Your Honor," said McCormack, "we will concede that Mr. Kunz, having been married to his wife for a number of years, has seen her handwriting before."

"All right," the judge said.

The technical quibbling over the notes took up most of the morning, with Branti pressing for identification of each individual note, while the actual content of the notes remained a mystery to the jury.

Finally, Branti walked up to the judge and said, "Your Honor, at this time I would like to have this series of notes entered into evidence."

McCormack rose quickly. "Your Honor, I just want the record to clearly reflect my objection to any testimony concerning these notes, on the grounds that any notes that a husband has procured allegedly written by his wife are confidential. Your Honor, I object to all of this."

"Your objection is noted, but I will allow the exhibits marked for identification."

222

Suddenly, loud sobbing disrupted the court. Kathy, who had been crying quietly in her seat, had lost control. Her body was shaking with grief. She stretched her arms across the table, buried her face between them, and wailed, "Peter, Peter, how can you do this to me?"

McCormack rested his hand on her shoulder. "Your Honor, may we take a short recess until my client is able to contain herself?"

When the courtroom emptied out, Alice, who had been mostly silent since the beginning of the trial, turned on her weeping daughter.

"He ain't worth all them tears, Kathy. I told ya before, the apple don't fall far from the tree. His ole man ain't no good and he ain't much better."

McCormack turned from his desk to look for his wife. He motioned to her. "Tess, please take Kathy to the rest room. See if you can get her to relax a little. The judge has only given us a ten-minute break."

"Come on Kathy, let's take a walk," offered Tess. "You need a break."

The squeaking sound of Alice's sneakers followed her distraught daughter into the hallway. At the nearest trash bucket, she lit a cigarette, her face a picture of consternation.

Leaning against the wall of the ladies' room, Kathy pushed away the wet paper towel the lawyer's wife handed her.

"My God, are they really going to send me to jail? How can these people, who know so little of my life, judge me? I still can't believe what Peter is doing! How could he, after all we've been through . . . after all those years?" She slid onto the cold tile floor, tears streaming down her cheeks and began to rock back and forth, crying like a child, calling her husband's name over and over.

"Kathy, you've got to pull yourself together. We can't help you if you don't help us." Kathy allowed Tess to press a cold towel to her forehead. Suddenly there was a knock on the door, and she heard her husband's voice: "Tess, we've got to get back in there, the judge is waiting!"

Kathy slowly got off the floor and straightened her clothes, went to the sink, and turned on the tap with force. She stared at the running water for a moment, as if she could lose herself in it, drown, and be carried away. She splashed the water on her face and looked in the mirror. The tears fell to her cheeks. When she emerged from the ladies' room, her ashen face was expressionless. *What is going to happen to me? What's going to happen to our baby?* In that moment, she could not fathom a life without Peter. She knew however, that her life was never going to be the same.

*   *   *

Meanwhile, in the corridor of the courthouse, the prosecutor saw McCormack pass the coffee station. "Hey, Mac," he shouted. "Want a cup of coffee?"

"No, thanks."

Branti quickly caught up to his courtroom adversary and asked in a confidential tone, "Level with me, Mac what's your strategy? Temporary insanity?"

McCormack smiled at Branti. He liked the younger man. He knew him to be was a tough, competent attorney. They had on occasion discussed the law over a drink at the local bar across from the courthouse but, they had never been confidants, and now was not the time for change.

Branti pressed on, "Why don't you make it easy on yourself and use the insanity plea? You'd save everyone a helluva lot of time and trouble! Wouldn't you rather be on a stream, fishing?"

McCormack smiled at him. "As a matter of fact, there's nothing I would like better, but right now I've got a job to do."

As McCormack walked away, he considered Branti's words. He had given a lot of thought to the insanity plea as an obvious and logical defense strategy, but it was not a simple matter. Were he to take that route, the court would recommend that Kathy be institutionalized and Peter, as the father of baby Cara, would be awarded custody. Would that be justice? McCormack thought not. The best way to achieve justice, he felt, was through the hearts of the jurors.

Alice sat in the corridor, waiting, blowing smoke down the hallway.

McCormack stopped and had a cigarette with her. He looked out the large, narrow windows behind her, at the gray sky and the courtyard below and realized it had been snowing for some time. The shrubs and walkways were already blanketed white.

He thought about Branti's remark about fishing and wondered what effect the late snow would have on the opening day of trout season. April, he realized, was not that far away.

With that comforting thought, he returned to the courtroom.

CHAPTER 33

1975

McCormack stood up and fixed his eyes on the well-groomed, dapper young man in the witness chair, conservatively dressed in a gray pinstriped suit, white shirt, and gray tie. He had made it clear from the start that he did not plan to be a hostile witness, that he would cooperate and tell the truth. McCormack cleared his throat and began the cross-examination.

"Mr. Kunz, when the clerk asked your address, you gave your *legal* address. Is that where you actually reside?"

"No, I stay mostly elsewhere." He gave an address in Tenafly, New Jersey.

"And do you stay there mostly with somebody?"

"Yes, Penny Belknap."

"Who lives at the other address?"

"My parents."

McCormack asked Peter about his trip to Haiti.

"Yes," Peter said, "I planned to take my wife with me, but then I met Penny and invited her instead." He acknowledged that she spent the entire six weeks living with him, and that upon his return to the States he had visited her every other weekend.

"Who took care of your business while you were in Haiti?"

"My wife."

"Did you pay her a salary for her services?"

"You mean my wife? No!"

"Did you pay anyone for their services?"

"Objection!" shouted Branti.

"Sustained," The Judge gave McCormack a look.

McCormack continued. "Is Miss Belknap your full-time employee now?"

"No," Peter replied calmly. "She only works when there is a special project. She works on a freelance basis."

"Does she receive pay?"

"Yes."

McCormack glanced at his papers before turning back to the witness box. "Now, I believe you testified that you returned home on the evening following the assault, at approximately ten p.m. and commenced looking for some notes. Is that correct?"

"Yes," he replied, "but I would like to amend something."

"You wish to amend your testimony from that of this morning?" asked McCormack, with questioning eyebrows.

"No, just the time I went looking for the notes. It was sometime in the early morning hours, like two or three o'clock."

"After your wife had gone to sleep?"

"Yes."

"And after you searched all the garbage upstairs, you went to the garage. Is that correct?"

"Yes."

"How many garbage bins did you search?"

"All of them."

One of the jurors handed the sheriff's deputy a note. She passed it to the judge. He quickly read it and looked out the snow-covered windows. McCormack and Branti exchanged glances.

"The Jury has expressed concern over the weather conditions," said Judge Gallucci. "Perhaps they are right." He banged his gavel. "Court will adjourn until ten o'clock tomorrow morning."

Tess waited for her husband in the hallway. When he didn't appear, she returned to the courtroom to look for him. From the doorway she could see him sitting alone at the defense table, flipping his pencil. She knew he was troubled.

"Gil," she called. "Are you going back to the office?"

He did not look up. His reply was sharp: "No."

"What's the matter?" She put her hands on his shoulders. She could feel the tenseness in his neck. "I thought your direct went well, didn't you?"

He had a troubled look on his face. "Did you see the jurors' look of approval when Peter corrected the time of his scavenger hunt? All that sincerity is tough to beat. Now I know why he came to see me before the trial asking me to help his wife and his mother-in-law. This guy doesn't believe he's done anything wrong! Remember all those pictures of his

227

girlfriend, all the letters that they wrote to each other that he showed Kathy? This guy thought he was being honest, not cruel! Peter's living between two worlds: one his father taught him, and the one where the rest of us live. He's a hell of a witness, Tess, and that's damn hard to beat!"

*   *   *

The next morning, Peter sat on the edge of the witness chair, looking less confident than the day before. His hands were clasped in his lap as he waited for the questioning to begin.

McCormack slowly approached him, flipping pencil in hand. "How long had you known Kathy before you married her?" His voice was soft and fatherly.

"About six months."

"And how old was she when you married?"

"Fifteen."

"Where did you go to live after you married?"

"With my parents."

"And at that time, was it the habit of your father to write letters and notes and keep a diary?"

"Yes."

"Did your father request that both you and your wife write notes and keep diaries?"

"Request?" Peter repeated. "He demanded it."

"And isn't it true that, in corresponding with each other, within the same household, you confided your innermost thoughts in writing?"

"Yes."

"After you moved from your parents' home, would you say Mrs. Kunz continued the practice of writing her innermost thoughts on paper?"

"Yes."

"So, you certainly knew, in October 1973, about your wife's propensity, inclination to write down her thoughts. Isn't that true?"

"Yes."

"And isn't it also true, Mr. Kunz, that during the years you were married, your wife regularly used a certain type of notepad in which she wrote these thoughts?"

"Yes."

McCormack's voice was strong. "Did you make carbon copies of letters to your friends and loved ones, which you wrote in a similar notepad... letters that revealed your own innermost thoughts...and show them to your wife?"

Peter appeared confused. Hesitantly, he questioned, "Which I kept carbon copies of? Ah, yes."

Branti objected trying to deter McCormack from establishing Peter's own propensities for writing, but before the morning session was over, the jury was well aware of it.

"Mr. Kunz, this habit of writing . . . I'll rephrase that. Did your father encourage your writing before your marriage?"

"Yes, we all wrote notes."

The Judge interrupted McCormack's questioning with a question of his own. "Did you and your wife do this throughout your marriage?"

Peter turned to look at the Judge and quietly replied, "Yes, sir. We did."

"So," continued the Judge, "you knew she wrote notes, you knew your father wrote notes, and they knew *you* wrote notes, too! Is that correct?"

"Yes, sir." He repeated. "That's true."

McCormack continued. "Now, Mr. Kunz, after you pieced the notes together, you drove to see Miss Belknap at the Nyack Hospital. That was, I believe, Monday, October 29, and you showed her your handiwork, did you not?"

"I showed her the notes, yes."

"Then you made three copies and mailed one copy to your friend Bill Vaughn?"

"Yes."

"What return address did you use?"

"My parents'."

"Were you present when Chief O'Shea visited Miss Belknap at the hospital on October 30?"

"Yes."

"And were you also present when she prepared a written statement against your wife?"

229

"No, I was not."

"Maybe I should rephrase that question. Were you present with her the entire day of October 30?"

"Yes."

"But you have no recollection of seeing a statement which Miss Belknap signed and gave to the chief of police?"

"No."

A loud noise disrupted the measured rhythm of McCormack's cross-examination. Branti had abruptly pushed his wooden chair away from the table and stood before the judge. "Sir, may I have a moment before Mr. McCormack continues?" He turned and, pointing to the defense attorney, pleaded: "He asked me for something awhile back, and I would like time to find it. I can't listen to his questions and look for it at the same time."

The Judge seemed perplexed. "Mr. Branti, if I were you, I would sit down and wait to see if he asks you for it again. You can look for it at that time."

Branti silently took his seat.

The Judge looked at the defense attorney. "You may continue."

McCormack walked over to the court clerk and handed her a document. When she returned it to him, he walked over to the witness and asked, "Mr. Kunz, do you recognize the signature on this document?"

"Yes, it's Penny's."

"Were you present on October 30 when she signed it?"

"Yes," Peter replied with downcast eyes, "I was present on October 30. But I don't remember her signing it."

"But you did, on that day, give the chief of police your own handiwork, the notes you so carefully and skillfully pieced together?"

With downcast eyes, he quietly replied. "Yes."

Branti was back on his feet. "I object to the term 'handiwork,' Your Honor."

The Judge turned to look at the jurors. "Disregard the characterization 'handiwork,' please."

Turning back to Peter, he asked, "But, you did show Chief O'Shea the pieces of paper you'd put together, didn't you?"

"Yes, sir, I did."

McCormack smiled at the judge. "I apologize for my use of the term 'handiwork,' but in my defense, he did use his hands."

Muffled laughter was heard from the spectators before the judge chided, "Again, the jury will disregard counsel's comments. They are not evidence."

"Mr. Kunz, did there come a time, shortly after your marriage, when Mrs. Kunz became pregnant?"

"Yes."

"By the way, Mr. Kunz, your father works with his hands. Is that correct?"

"Yes."

McCormack opened his large black briefcase and removed an unusual-looking, shiny object. The jurors leaned forward, but McCormack kept it mostly concealed, holding it close to his chest. He slowly approached the witness chair. In a soft voice, he asked, "Mr. Kunz, have you ever seen this instrument before?"

Peter's reaction was swift. He closed his eyes, as if not seeing. His voice barely audible, "Yes."

"Did your father use this tool to perform an abortion on your teenage wife?"

"Objection, Your Honor!" Branti leaped to his feet. "Objection!"

As the protest continued, Kathy began to cry. She put her head on the table, wrapped her arms around her head, recalling the day she had hidden the abortion tool, determined never to allow Oskar to use it on her again. It was still hidden in her shoebox. She felt a pang of guilt remembering the abuse Hanna had taken from Oskar for her 'stupidity and carelessness' in misplacing it.

She heard the judge say, "If Mr. Kunz knows the answer to the question, I will let him answer."

'Yes"

"Did your father also tell you that before he performed an abortion on your wife, who was only sixteen at the time, he had sexual relations with her?"

"Objection, Your Honor!" Branti shouted.

"I'll let him answer if he knows."

Peter shifted in his chair. Looking very uncomfortable, he asked, "Could you repeat that question, please?" The court stenographer read it to him, but he continued to look confused.

He was quiet for a moment. He looked at the defense lawyer. "You mean, you want to know if I knew he had sex with her?"

"Yes," replied McCormack.

Peter was obviously rattled. He asked, "At what time, the second time?"

McCormack pressed, "I ask you again, did your father tell you that, before he performed an abortion on your wife, he had sexual relations with her?"

"He told me he had to."

"And he did perform an abortion?"

"Yes."

"With your knowledge and consent?"

"Objection, Your Honor!"

"Overruled."

Peter answered, "Well, let's just say, with my knowledge."

"And isn't it a fact that the second time your wife became pregnant, she waited until well into her second trimester before she told you she was pregnant?"

"Yes, she did wait a long time."

"And isn't it a fact that your father angrily denounced this second pregnancy and as a result of his actions, your wife lost this child as well?"

"Yes."

By the time court adjourned that day, Peter looked exhausted.

*   *   *

Later that evening, as the McCormacks discussed the trial at dinner, Tess said to her husband, "You know, Gil, I've been watching the jurors, and I notice some of them seem to have developed a real rapport. Juror six, Ann something or other, you know, the schoolteacher with the long black hair."

"Ann Polanski?"

"Yes. And, you know the good-looking guy who sits behind her? I think his name is Dalton. I've noticed she's always turning around and smiling at him. During lunch breaks they walk together to the restaurant and really seem to enjoy each other's company."

"They have a lot in common. They're both schoolteachers."

"I thought he was a salesman."

"Only part-time."

"Well, anyway, I have the feeling they'll be on your side. I think if you get one, you'll probably get the other."

"I wouldn't count on that. Jurors are funny. Very unpredictable."

"There's also another interesting duo. Have you noticed the two elderly jurors, the white-haired lady—she's a retired writer—and the tall, gray-haired man who sits next to her? I like the way he looks at her. You never can tell—maybe you've sparked a new romance."

"I haven't exactly had time to worry about playing Cupid."

"I wonder what their reaction is to Oskar's philosophy."

"I hope they get to hear it all. I don't know how much I can get in before Branti has a stroke."

*   *   *

The next morning, Peter appeared in court looking well rested. Kathy, on the other hand, looked gaunt and haggard wearing the same black dress she had worn the day before. Her eyes revealed the depths of her despair.

McCormack continued with his examination, painting a picture of two young lovers, Kathy and Peter, leaving on a trip to Colorado, a vacation interrupted by the demands of a possessive father; and a new start in their first apartment.

McCormack knew he had the jurors' attention when he asked, "Mr. Kunz, what happened when you again began working for your father?"

"Well, sometimes, when I had to work late, I'd stay overnight."

"Was there anything in particular that occurred during that period?" continued McCormack.

233

Sweat beads appeared on Peter's forehead. Falteringly, he asked, "Would you repeat the question, please?"

"I'll withdraw the question," McCormack said in a fatherly tone. Peter looked relieved.

Then, McCormack quickly turned back. "By the way, Mr. Kunz, do you have a sister?"

"Yes."

"Is her name Ingrid?"

"Yes."

"Do you also have a half-sister named Janice?"

Peter's eyes widened, the look of alarm returning. He glanced at Branti, who sat calmly, not realizing the implication of the question.

Peter did not respond, so McCormack asked again, "Well, do you?"

"Yes."

"Is she, in fact, your father's illegitimate daughter?"

Branti now leaped to his feet. "Objection, Your Honor, this line of questioning is out of order."

"Sustained."

McCormack walked back to his desk, picked up his pencil, and began flipping it, his face tense.

Peter sat nervously waiting for the next question. McCormack leaned on the wooden railing of the witness box, staring into Peter's eyes. In a booming voice that startled everyone in the courtroom, he asked, "And isn't it a fact, Mr. Kunz, that, while you were working with your father, sleeping in his house, you were having a love affair with your sister Janice?"

Peter's voice was clear. "Yes."

The court exploded in pandemonium.

Branti leaped to his feet, as he was wont to do, shouting his objection. Holding a handkerchief over her mouth, the white-haired woman juror started to choke and cough. Other jurors sat stunned. Alice shouted an obscenity, and the judge pounded his gavel for order.

Her eyes focused on her husband, Kathy seemed to have neither heard nor noticed the commotion. She could not have expressed what she was seeing or feeling—not then, for it was too strangely unfamiliar—but she already sensed that something lodged deep in her heart had given way.

McCormack quietly sat down.

Court was adjourned.

*   *   *

The strain of three days of testimony was beginning to show on Peter's face. McCormack wasted no time in refreshing the jurors' memory of the events that had led to the abrupt adjournment.

"It was after this illicit affair with your sister that you and your wife bought the house in Piermont. Is that correct?"

"Yes."

"And it was shortly after that, when you had an assignment to work in Boston, that you met Penny Belknap?"

"Yes."

"And is it also a fact that you urged your wife to meet Penny with exhortations such as 'If you meet her, I know you will like her'?"

"Yes, I guess I did say something like that."

"When did you first learn of your wife's most recent pregnancy?"

"As soon as I came back from Haiti."

"Did you suggest an abortion at that time?"

"Yes, I did."

"And did you subsequently discuss having 'our baby' with Miss Belknap?"

"Well," Peter hesitated, "that was just. . . I guess I did say something like that."

"Do you recall, while your wife was pregnant, she told you she was so upset about your relationship with Penny that she was consulting a psychiatrist?"

"Yes."

"Did she ask you to go with her—to help her?"

"Yes."

"And did you?"

"Once."

"And then what happened?"

235

"I didn't like him meddling in my personal affairs and I stopped going."

"Mr. Kunz, did you at any time tell anyone that you were going to have Katherine institutionalized and take the baby from her?"

"No!"

"I have no further questions, Your Honor."

CHAPTER 34

1975

The next day, McCormack arrived at the courthouse late. Tess met him in the hallway.

"Gil, where have you been? They're waiting for you."

"There was a serious accident on Main Street; tied up traffic for a mile."

"There's a man in the courtroom setting up a big projector."

"I'm not surprised. Branti is still trying to get the jurors to see those notes. Where are Kathy and Mrs. Jackson?"

"They're already in there."

"Good." McCormack turned to walk into the courtroom.

"Gil, wait. I want to tell you something."

"Can't it wait, Tess? I'm already late."

"This is important. First, Kathy seems much better today. She actually talked to me and acted normal. Second, today is Baby Cara's first birthday."

A faint smile appeared on McCormack's face. As Tess followed him into the courtroom, she whispered under her breath, "I thought you'd like that."

* * *

"Good morning, counselor," Branti greeted. "I thought maybe you might have gone fishing."

"It won't be long now."

Branti knew the most damning evidence was yet to come. The jury had heard a lot about the notes, and now they would see the notes for themselves. He had had large slides made of each, and the handwriting expert would be his last witness.

He realized that McCormack had held the jury spellbound with his tales of abortion and illicit sex but was convinced that the notes were the only real evidence in the case. They were the clearest proof of her intent to murder Penny. *Dig hole deeper,* one note had said; he smiled as the deputy announced the arrival of the judge.

Branti had prepared well and he had the smell of victory in his nostrils. He smiled as the deputy announced the arrival of the Judge.

He began with directing the juror's attention to a large screen that had been set in clear view of the jurors. Branti knew the notes were damning and he wanted the jurors to see all of them. His first witness was a handwriting expert. Once his credentials were established, Branti addressed the judge. He called the handwriting expert to the stand. A tall man in his late fifties entered the room impeccably dressed.

"Your Honor, at this time, I would like to offer these notes into evidence."

McCormack slowly rose to his feet and approached the bench. He knew this was an important moment as he addressed the Judge: "Your Honor, I would like to renew my objection to admitting these notes into evidence on the grounds that they are a form of confidential communication between husband and wife."

The judge again listened to McCormack's attempt to suppress the notes and finally agreed to hold a suppression hearing behind closed doors. The hearing was brief, McCormack's motion denied.

When court resumed, the handwriting expert was ready, standing in front of the screen, pointer in hand, signaling the projectionist to begin.

"Your Honor," McCormack began, "may I approach the bench? I would like to make a statement on behalf of my client."

Branti sat up in his chair, a look of annoyance on his face.

"At this time, sir, I wish to advise the jury that the notes were written by the defendant, Katherine Kunz. She does not deny, nor has she ever denied writing them. Her only denial is in the interpretation of them. They are just the fantasy of a woman under a lot of stress."

Branti jumped to his feet, the veins in his neck visible. "Fantasy, hell!" he bellowed. "It's a shopping list for *murder!*"

The judge banged his gavel for order.

McCormack continued, "In the interest of time, for the sake of the jurors who have sat so patiently and attentively throughout this trial, I withdraw my objection to the notes. Since my client acknowledges the handwriting as her own, there is no need for a handwriting analyst."

Once again, Branti objected. "Your Honor, this witness came all the way from New York City to testify today and I feel it is imperative that the jury hear his testimony."

The judge removed his glasses and looked down from the bench. "Mr. Branti, since the defense counsel has admitted his client wrote the notes, the need for the expert is superfluous. The witness is excused."

"But Your Honor…"

"Do you have any other witnesses, Mr. Branti?" asked the judge.

"No, sir. The prosecution rests."

* * *

"The defense calls Alice Jackson to the stand."

Alice stood up, clutching the cardigan draped loosely over her cotton housedress. She shuffled her way up to the witness chair, her corrective shoes emphasizing her flat-footed gait. She wore no makeup. The only hint of glamour was a rhinestone bobby pin that held her straight, cropped hair to one side.

She appeared fragile, but her tone was aggressive and hostile. She resented having to testify. She told the court she was a widow with nine living children and fifteen grandchildren. 'After the kids growed up,' she had saved her money by working as a live-in housekeeper and cook in the St. John's rectory in Brooklyn, a position she had held for some seven years.

When her daughter and son-in-law wanted to buy a house, she had 'loaned' them two thousand dollars, which they had promised to repay. "They ain't never given me back one red cent," she said bitterly. "That's why Peter offered to pay my lawyer's fee, 'cause his conscience wuz botherin' him."

McCormack asked, "Did you know your daughter and son-in-law were having marital difficulties?"

"I don't know nothin' 'bout their business. I only saw Kathy crying a lot, and I knew sometin' wuz wrong, but she didn't tell me nothin'."

"Did Kathy tell you she was going to visit Peter's girlfriend?"

"Are you kiddin'? She wouldn't tell me nothin' like that, 'cause she knew I'd tell her she wuz nuts."

"Were you aware that your daughter was in the habit of writing notes?"

"Sure, she wuz always writin' sometin'. She and Peter used to write to each other all the time. Sometimes I'd tell her if she didn't write herself a note, she'd forget to go to the bathroom."

Loud laughter broke the silence of the courtroom; even the jurors smiled.

"Did you ever read any of her notes?" McCormack asked.

"What fer? It weren't none of my business." Then, as an afterthought, she mumbled, "Guess maybe I shouda—I might not be sittin' here right now."

"Would you tell the jury what happened on the night Kathy brought Miss Belknap to your home?"

"Nothin' much, at first. I cooked dinner, but she didn't eat much—just picked. We watched television. Then Kathy told her to sleep in my room so the cats and dogs wouldn't bother her. Ya see the animals don't come in my room, 'cause they know I always kick 'em out. So, me and Kathy slept together."

"What happened the following morning?"

"I wuz the first one up and made coffee. I can't do nothing' witout my coffee and cigarettes. Then I heard Kathy running to the bathroom, throwin' up, and a few minutes later that broad came in the kitchen. I asked her nice if she wanted coffee, but she jes' wanted juice. I said, 'Help yerself.' She looked mad, and I figured she's upset 'cause Kathy's sick and I know she's in a hurry to go to see Peter. She sits down to watch TV, and the next thing I know she's comin' at me with a hammer! Now, I may look dumb, but I ain't stupid, so I jumped off my stool and ducked under the counter. She swung over the counter so hard she hit her hand on the edge and dropped the hammer. I grabbed it quick and held on to it. I never did let go till the cops came."

"Where was Kathy while all this was going on?"

"She wuz still in the bathroom, throwin' up. When she heard the noise, she came running and tried to help me. She took the frying pan off the stove and popped her one!"

"Did you ever strike Penny?"

"Yer darn right I did. Wouldn't ya? She had some nerve. I cooked for her, gave her my bed, and then she tried to kill me!"

"Did you at *any time* make plans with your daughter, written or otherwise, to murder Penny Belknap?"

"No! I never hurt nobody in my whole life!"

"Your Honor, I have no further questions."

CHAPTER 35

1975

Although the day had started with a chill, by lunchtime most of the snow was gone and the sun was sparkling off the Hudson with a promise of spring.

The sheriff's deputy shepherded the jurors to the restaurant directly across from the courthouse. They were a happy group, pleased to have been chosen for such an interesting trial and comfortable in each other's company. As they entered the restaurant, Baby Cara's head popped up from a booth in the corner. Kathy's sister Anna quickly pulled her down, knowing that even the restaurant had been designated off-limits for them. But today was a special day-- Cara's birthday-- and Anna wanted to surprise Kathy and their mother.

The jurors turned to look at Baby Cara as they passed. Some smiled at her, others turned away.

A table had been reserved for the jurors in the far corner of the dining room. The two schoolteachers sat side by side, in full agreement that the trial was far more fascinating than anything they'd ever seen happen in their classrooms. Across the table from them, the two retirees were engrossed in an amicable chat of their own.

When Gil McCormack entered the restaurant, he saw the jurors seated in the corner. He also saw Anna and the baby. He turned to his wife. "I think we'd better get them out of here. Tell Anna, if she wants to join us for lunch, we'll be across the street. I'll wait outside for Kathy and Mrs. Jackson."

A few minutes later, the lunch arrangements squared away, McCormack turned to Alice seated next to him at the table and smiled. "Mrs. Jackson, you did very well this morning."

"Yeah?" She grinned. "Ya really think I did good?"

"Very good. Just remember, when Mr. Branti cross-examines you this afternoon, answer 'yes' or 'no' whenever you can. And don't offer any *information*. Relax, and don't let him get you nervous."

"That macaroni head-- he isn't going to get me nervous."

242

Branti had taken copious notes during Alice's direct examination, but his objections had been few. Now, he tried unsuccessfully to get Alice to admit that she knew her daughter was going to Massachusetts and had conspired with her.

"What did you think that large hole was for in the backyard?"

"I don't pay it no mind. The way them damn dogs dig up the yard and mess out there, ya think I go walking' out there? I got enough trouble with these feet jess' walking on flat ground."

"Mrs. Jackson, you testified this morning that your daughter was always writing notes. Do you expect this jury to believe that you live in the same house with your daughter and that you never read any of her notes?"

"I don't say I never read any of 'em, but I just don't go 'round the house reading everythin' she writes, Mr. Macaroni!"

"The name is Branti."

McCormack smiled at Alice's slip.

"Excuse me," said Alice, "but I don't think ya understand. Ya see, if ya knowed me . . . ya'd know I can't read witout my glasses and I can't walk wit them on, 'cause they make me dizzy. So, I only wear 'em when I'm sittin' down. Now do you understand?"

"Mrs. Jackson, isn't it a fact that you felt sorry for your daughter, and when you saw that she was sick, you decided to get rid of Penny for her?"

"Are ya crazy? Did ya see how big she is? I'll admit I've been in a few scraps in my day, but I ain't stupid. She's a very strong broad. I wuz lucky she didn't kill me!"

Branti walked back to his desk and riffled through his notes.

Frustrated though not angry, he finally turned, looked at the judge, and admitted, "Your Honor, I have no further questions."

243

CHAPTER 36

1975

"The defense calls Katherine Kunz to the stand."

She rose on shaking legs and made her way to the witness box.

McCormack smiled at her. His voice was encouraging. "Mrs. Kunz, I want you to relax and keep your voice up so that all the jurors can hear you."

She tried to return his smile and failed. She could not accept McCormack's assurance that everything would be all right. So far, nothing had been all right. Her own husband had testified against her. Notes she had written to herself in the privacy of her own bedroom had been made public and would be used against her.

Her face felt frozen. *How could anyone relax under these circumstances?* She looked around the room and saw rows upon rows of strange, blank faces staring back at her. How could he say relax, everything will be all right? How could he be so sure? A chill ran down her spine, and her hands began to sweat. She dug them deep into her lap and began to tug on her fingers.

When McCormack asked questions, she heard herself answer, but the sound of her own voice seemed unfamiliar and muffled. She had come to realize that even if Peter had honestly tried, for all those years, he probably never really did love her. This realization crushed her, and she began to cry.

"Mrs. Kunz, please," McCormack pleaded again. "Keep your voice up. The jurors can't hear you."

"Do you remember the first time you became pregnant after you and Peter were married?" McCormack's pencil started to flip. The jurors watched.

Kathy stared. She nodded her answer.

"Will you please tell the jury what happened when you first told your father-in-law, Oskar Kunz, you were pregnant? The pencil flipped. He caught it without looking.

244

The mere mention of Oskar's name caused Kathy's mouth to twitch nervously. She stared at her attorney, saw the pencil flipping, but made no reply.

Vaguely she heard Branti objecting, being overruled. She looked at the jury box. Twelve hostile faces glared back at her. She looked at the clock. How much longer am I going to be here? She needed to get out of here. How many more questions is he going to ask? *I need a sedative. I need something.* She couldn't stand this badgering anymore. She forgot the question.

McCormack walked up to her chair, a concerned expression on his face.

Kathy had slumped deep into her chair, her pupils dilated, her face contorted with fear. She seemed confused.

"Your Honor," McCormack said, "I believe Mrs. Kunz needs a break. Could we recess for lunch?"

When the judge called the recess, Kathy jumped from her seat and ran from the courtroom.

McCormack slammed his briefcase shut and joined his wife in the rear of the courtroom, frustration clearly etched on his face. "What the hell's the matter with her? Getting answers from her is suddenly like pulling teeth. Would you please go find her and tell her we're running out of time?"

When Tess found her, Kathy had locked herself in the backseat of her car. Alice was banging on the window. Kathy refused to come out or even roll down the window. Instead, she took a sedative, curled up on the seat and went to sleep for the duration of the recess.

When court convened, McCormack began with caution. "Mrs. Kunz, I want you to relax and answer my questions so the jury can hear you. Do you understand?"

She nodded her head.

Slowly he coaxed Kathy to tell the jury her story of the events that led up to and included the alleged assault. Now the jurors had heard everyone's versions. Then he changed the subject. He was going to go back and ask about her life in Oskar's house.

"Mrs. Kunz, you've already testified that your father-in-law became angry when you became pregnant. Please tell the jury what he did."

Kathy immediately started to shake. She tugged at her fingers and started to cry. "He said I had to have an abortion."

"Tell the jury what he did next."

She stared at him but made no reply.

McCormack leaned into the witness box trying to make eye contact. "Mrs. Kunz, please tell the jury. . . did your father-in-law perform an abortion on you?"

Kathy slumped in her chair, her face contorted with fear. She couldn't answer that: they'd twist it; they would use it against her, just like Oskar did. They wouldn't believe her anyway. Nobody believed her. . . even her lawyer didn't believe her!

"Mrs. Kunz, please tell the jury. . . did your father-in-law perform an abortion on you when he learned of your pregnancy?"

Kathy lowered her head and looked away.

McCormack's voice boomed and startled her. "Please answer yes or no!"

"Yes." She whispered.

McCormack walked back to the defense table and picked up his pencil. Kathy watched him flip and catch it without looking.

He turned and quietly asked, "And did he force you to have sex with him first?"

She slouched lower in her chair, her face wet with perspiration, nodding her head.

"And did your husband force you to continue to have sex with your father-in-law?"

She lifted her chin, tugged on her fingers and suddenly shouted, "Yes, he did!! Yes, he did!!" Tears fell to her cheeks and she slid lower in her seat.

Kathy heard McCormack's questions and suddenly she felt as if she was caught in the grip of an old nightmare, her energy draining away. *Look at him! What's he doing? Why is he asking me all these questions? He knows I can't answer them. And why is Oskar here?*

McCormack realized his client was in serious trouble. She looked to be on the verge of collapse. He knew she could not continue. He turned to the Judge. "Your Honor, in view of the lateness of the hour, I respectfully request an adjournment until morning. "

The judge glanced at the clock. It was four thirty-five. He removed his glasses, rubbed his eyes, and asked, "Can you conclude your examination before five?"

"No, Your Honor, I cannot. I believe my client needs medical attention."

"All right, then." Judge Gallucci banged his gavel. "Court is adjourned."

* * *

Kathy drove home at an insane speed in the wet, slushy snow, her mother screaming at her to slow down. She went into the bathroom, picked up a bottle of sedatives and to Alice's horror, emptied it into her mouth.

That evening, Kathy's psychiatrist, Dr. Alexander, made a house call. He spent several hours with her.

He told McCormack that a combination of things had caused her breakdown: too many sedatives, anxiety, and McCormack's flipping pencil. Kathy had focused on the movement and had gone into a trance, seeing Oskar's pointed finger reminding her of her promise: "What goes on in this house stays in this house."

The doctor agreed to see her again in the morning before nine.

When court resumed the next day, Kathy appeared rested, the red dress she had chosen to wear lending a slight color to her pale, unmade-up face. She promised to answer his questions.

McCormack's examination of her was brief. He began with what happened at the house. "While Penny Belknap slept in your mother's room, did you or any member of your family try to harm her?"

"No."

"Did you ever try to hide or conceal your true identity from Penny Belknap?"

"No."

"Did you ever plot or plan, individually or with someone, to kill Penny Belknap?"

"No."

"Day before yesterday was a very special and emotional day for you, was it not?"

"Yes."

"Would you mind telling the jurors why it had such a special meaning for you?"

"It was my daughter's first birthday."

"I have no further questions, Your Honor."

*   *   *

Branti walked up to the witness and smiled, "Good morning, Mrs. Kunz. Are you feeling stronger today?"

"Yes, sir."

"Now, Mrs. Kunz, I will show you these documents, which you have acknowledged were written by you." Branti held up a piece of paper that had been Scotch-taped together.

"This one says something I don't quite understand. *Diddle the telephone.* Can you tell the jury what you meant by that?"

"I don't remember. The kitchen phone never worked right."

"Is it because you tampered with it so that Miss Belknap could not use it to call for help?"

"No, it just never worked right."

"Did you ever report it to the phone company?"

"No."

Branti walked toward the jurors, still smiling. He held the notes high above his head. *"Make sure Peter sleeps all night!* Now, Mrs. Kunz, if, as you have testified, Peter wanted you to meet Penny, why didn't you tell him you were going to Boston, instead of sneaking out in the middle of the night while he slept?"

"Because I wanted to meet her alone for the first time, to... to see for myself what she looked like... to see what she was like, first. Besides, I still wasn't sure, in my mind, whether I was going to see her or my sister Anna. I was confused and upset. I didn't really know where I was going."

Branti flipped through a few more notes before he read, *"Dig deep hole,"* his voice dropping on the word *deep.* He looked up at the witness and asked, "How deep did you want the hole, Mrs. Kunz?"

"I didn't dig it, the kids did. I had no idea how big it was."

"But you told them to dig it *deep,* so that it would be deep enough for Miss Belknap's body, isn't that right?"

"Objection, Your Honor" McCormack shouted.

"Sustained."

Branti's determination to get all the notes before the jury finally succeeded. He read every note, word for word, demanding explanations and clarifications along the way. When he finished, he walked past McCormack's table, and smiled.

* * *

The noonday sun was warm and bright when luncheon recess was called, but Kathy was too ill to notice. She rushed into the ladies' room and vomited, then, once again, took refuge in her car. Before returning to the courtroom, she fortified herself with a sip of coffee and another sedative.

Branti picked up where he left off. "Mrs. Kunz, you testified you struck Miss Belknap with an iron skillet to protect your mother. Is that correct?"

"Yes."

"When your neighbor Mr. Pelligrino came to the front door, why didn't you tell him Miss Belknap tried to kill your mother, instead of just slamming the door in his face?"

"At that moment, I was upset and confused, and I really didn't know what I was doing."

"But you knew *enough* to resume the attack as soon as you closed the door, didn't you?"

"I don't remember doing that. I only remember feeling sick and being scared. I really don't remember very much of what happened that day. My mind was a blur."

By mid-afternoon, the strain of the pounding examination had taken its toll, and Kathy again began tugging on her fingers again, her face flushed and her mouth twitching nervously.

McCormack asked for a recess.

In the hallway, he tried to calm her down. Handing her a glass of water, he said, "You're doing fine. Just take your time—and remember, answer 'yes' or 'no' whenever possible. Save your energy... it's almost over."

He saw Branti by the coffee machine and walked over to him. "Do you think you can speed things up a bit? The trout are getting impatient."

But Branti was far from finished. Through a barrage of questions, he attempted to get Kathy to admit she had encouraged Peter's relationship with Penny. Steadfastly, she maintained that she never had, and that it had almost driven her insane.

"Isn't it a fact, Mrs. Kunz," Branti continued, "that it was only *after* Mr. Kunz asked you for a divorce that you decided to get rid of Miss Belknap?"

"No!" Kathy screamed as the tears again began to roll down her face.

"Isn't it a fact, Mrs. Kunz, that you planned to push Penny Belknap off the cliff on your way home from Boston but failed because too many people were around?"

"No!"

"And isn't it also a fact that you wanted to poison her, but she refused to drink the spiked juice?"

"No!"

"Isn't it a fact that Miss Belknap foiled your plans to kill her during the night by being awake when you entered her room?"

"No, that's not true. I—"

"And isn't it a fact that you passed your mother a note on the morning of the assault, which read, *After you finish your cigarette, hit her over the head with the hammer?*"

"No, no . . . no!" Kathy shook her head violently. "That's not true!"

Branti leaned over the railing and shouted into her face, "And isn't it also a fact, Mrs. Kunz, that you wanted Miss Belknap dead?"

Kathy sobbed audibly and looked at McCormack for help. The defense attorney sat still, the only movement a rhythmical, mesmerizing, hypnotizing flipping of the pencil.

Beads of perspiration covered Kathy's face. Her mouth was dry; she could barely move her lips. She closed her eyes tightly, trying to concentrate on the prosecutor's questions, overwhelmed by the intensity of her feelings.

"YES, YES, YES," Kathy cried, covering her face with her hands. "I wished her dead many times—in my mind." She removed her hands from her face and looked directly at the jurors. "But I couldn't kill her . . . I could never kill anyone!"

The room fell silent.

McCormack's pencil kept flipping.

Kathy fell down, down, down into the black whirlpool of oblivion and, for a moment, was grateful for it.

CHAPTER 37

1975

From the depths of her agony, Kathy watched McCormack approach the jury to deliver his summation. Every eye in the courtroom was on him now, every ear tuned in to his words. *He's got nothing to work with,* she thought, *and it's all my fault.* She knew she had been a disastrous witness. Why hadn't she been able to open up and tell the story that so needed telling? From the stand, all she had been able to see was a room full of strangers who knew nothing of her life yet held it in their hands. She should have told them more. She'd been afraid, so afraid, that they would take one little ill-chosen word and twist it against her. And if they put her away and took her baby from her, she would die. If it weren't for Cara, nothing would matter. She would let everything go down the drain, her life included.

McCormack slowly rises from the defense table. He doesn't seem to be in a hurry. He looks at the two defendants, they look frightened. Their burden weighs heavily on his shoulders. He knows their life depends on him. But he is ready. Many years ago, more than he cared to remember, he promised to help the helpless, and that moment had come. He walked slowly. He pointed to the defendants, his voice soft but commanding:

"Ladies and gentlemen of the jury, justice must be done, and you twelve ladies and gentlemen *are* justice now. Each of you must have the intelligence and the heart to render justice in this case.

"I know that Mr. Branti is a very competent prosecutor. I know he has waved the notes in front of you and quoted them up and down. I'm going to ask you to consider the circumstances under which they were written, and who it was that hunted for them through the garbage and saw to it that they got into the hands of the prosecution. It was Peter Kunz. What did he have to gain by so doing?

"Let's look at these notes." McCormack paused, his voice was softer—his cadence slower. "Are these the notes of a cold-blooded murderess? Or are they the disjointed ramblings of a poor, agitated, lovesick, pregnant woman? You can't consider them without considering what she was put through by her husband and father-in-law. She had been trapped in a den of iniquity and had to fight to survive. And she did fight: she had spunk; she struggled even through her husband's romantic involvement with his own half-sister; and the dream at last seemed to have come true. And what did Peter spring on her? Another girlfriend and another demand for an abortion! If ever there was a reason for a breakdown, Kathy Kunz had that reason.

"You've heard Peter Kunz testify on the witness stand that writing was a family habit. His father indoctrinated Kathy with the habit, teaching her, according to Peter's testimony, that if you had frustrations, you wrote them out of your system.

"When Mr. Branti quotes and re-quotes from these notes, remember the simple, harmless reason why they were written; remember to whose advantage it was to hunt through the garbage bins at three o'clock in the morning and piece them together!

"Kathy Kunz has told you that she was extremely upset and that she called a psychiatrist. She told her husband of her troubled state, begging for help. Did he help her? No, he shrugged her off. Honest Peter! He was so honest he bragged to his wife about his love affairs. But was he honest about the notes? Did he tell Kathy he found the notes and that he was going to give them to the police? Did he even go to the police himself? No, Honest Peter didn't want to be seen as the mastermind in the plot, so he waited until the police called on his girlfriend and then just happened to have the pieced-together notes with him.

"These notes were a fantasy to Kathy Kunz, written out of sheer frustration. She attached so little importance to them that she simply threw them away; she didn't burn them, or flush them down the toilet, *she simply threw them away*. Remember *that* when Mr. Branti tries to make a big thing out of them.

"Then, there's the wig and the dark glasses. I'm sure Mr. Branti will say she tried to use them as a disguise. Yet, remember the first thing she said when she met Penny Belknap: 'I'm Peter's wife, Kathy. It's time we had a talk.' The wig and glasses were just as harmless as the notes. Just as much a part of the fantasy."

McCormack paused. He knew he was reaching some of the jurors. He could see sympathy on their faces. Most, however, listened expressionless. He knew the defense attorney was listening carefully, too.

"There are many weaknesses in the prosecution's case, ladies and gentlemen, and I could go on and on, but it's been a long trial, and it has been a longer one for Kathy Kunz. She's been on trial since the day she married Peter Kunz.

"It's time to put an end to her ordeal." McCormack paused again, allowing the jury to think about that for a moment.

"As for Mrs. Jackson, why is she here at all? The only testimony we have is Penny Belknap's, and there is no substantiation whatsoever. Under no circumstances could justice be done on this kind of evidence, this *lack* of evidence."

McCormack leaned forward, placed his hands on the wooden railing before the jurors, his voice low.

"Remember, ladies and gentlemen, only you can prevent Peter Kunz and his girlfriend Penny Belknap from succeeding in their design to get rid of Kathy and get custody of Baby Cara. The only just verdict in this case has to be, *must be*, NOT GUILTY."

* * *

Branti rose to his feet and moved swiftly toward the jury, beaming with charisma. He straightened his jacket, walked to the divider that separated him from the jury. He took his time and smiled at the jurors. The spectators' silence was deafening. He looked meaningfully at each one of them.

"Ladies and gentlemen of the jury, I said earlier that a trial is nothing more than a search for truth. Now I ask to be your guide in search of that truth.

"No amount of sympathy for them can alter the two basic questions: did the defendants *attempt* to cause the death of Penny Belknap, and did they *intend* to cause it?

"The intent to kill, ladies and gentlemen, may be and usually is formed in one split second. Premeditation and planning are prerequisites

254

for murder. This is why this is a simple case-- because we have it right here."

Branti picked up the notes and waved them before the jurors. "It's all spelled out, in an elaborate plot, in great detail, and in the handwriting of this defendant." He pointed an accusatory finger at Kathy.

Kathy stared ahead, seeing no one, hearing nothing. She had retreated so far within herself that even the likelihood of going to jail didn't stir her.

"Great pains were taken to commit the crime of murder," Branti continued, his voice rising with excitement. "Great pains were taken, and a plan was carefully followed right down to the finest detail.

"Mr. McCormack says it's a fantasy. I say it's a shopping list for murder! Mr. McCormack would have you believe these notes are innermost thoughts. I say it's a diary of death!

"The defense has concocted a moving tale, but it is a fairytale. So," concluded Branti, "take the evidence in your hands, sift it, hold it up to the light. Thus, you will reach the truth. You will see two women, one who planned the crime in careful detail, and one who helped her carry it out. Those two women sit there at that table," he pointed an accusatory finger at them, "and I ask you now, in the cause of justice and on behalf of the people of this state, to find them GUILTY as charged."

CHAPTER 38

1975

The jury in the *People v. Kunz & Jackson* commenced deliberations early in the afternoon with a disagreement, not about the case but about the selection of a foreman. They had finally decided on Joe Turner, the construction worker, a married father of two children, over the bitter objections of Jon Dalton, who felt that he should have been chosen because of his prior experience on a criminal jury.

The erstwhile camaraderie thus fissured by a sour note, they settled down to business. As far as Alice Jackson's lack of involvement went, no one believed she conspired in a plot to murder Penny Belknap.

"Just to speed things up," the foreman said, "let's take a secret vote to see how many of us agree about the guilt or innocence of Kathy Kunz."

All agreed Kathy was guilty, of something. No one was in favor of acquittal. But, six believed her guilty of attempted murder; three felt the verdict should be assault in the first degree; and two voted for assault in the second degree. Eleanor Evans, the retired writer, had voted for simple assault.

At midnight, with tempers flaring, the foreman had sent a note to Judge Gallucci.

By that time, the crowded courtroom had fallen silent, the clock above the jury box impartially measuring off the last moments of suspense. The defendants sat transfixed: Kathy so still as to appear asleep; Alice glowering at the judge, her eyes clear and alert, almost defiant.

The judge seemed perplexed by the note handed to him. He glanced at the cranky jurors then silently reread it. Removing his dark, horn-rimmed glasses, he addressed the foreman.

"I have read your note and find it confusing. Is it my understanding that the jury wishes to continue its deliberations in the morning?"

"That is correct, Your Honor."

"And is it my further understanding that the jury has reached a partial verdict?"

"Yes, Your Honor."

The judge turned toward the two women. "Will the defendants please rise?"

Alice rose quickly. Kathy appeared frozen in her chair. McCormack assisted her to her feet.

The judge addressed the older woman first.

"Alice Jackson, the jury finds you not guilty of attempted murder but finds you guilty of assault in the third degree.

"Katherine Kunz, the jury finds you guilty, but at this time, the jurors have been unable to determine the degree of your guilt."

The word *guilty* pierced McCormack like a sword. Kathy's ordeal was to continue. Everything now hinged upon the *degree* of her guilt.

Neither defendant moved. They stared at the judge, not yet fully comprehending what was happening. Judge Gallucci turned to the jury foreman and asked, "Is that correct?"

"Yes, Your Honor, that is the way the jury finds it."

The crowd of spectators rustled with gasps and whispers. Reporters raced for the door, hoping to make the deadline.

The two women were still on their feet. Kathy turned to stare at the jurors, shaking her head, whether in disbelief, reproach, or confusion-- it was hard to tell.

The judge rapped his gavel for silence.

"At this time, ladies and gentlemen, I will accept a partial verdict with respect to the defendant Kunz, and you will be sequestered for one more night, with a reminder not to listen to the radio, watch TV, or read any newspapers lest your impartiality is compromised by the news coverage. In the morning, you can continue with your deliberations."

McCormack rose. "Your Honor, for the sake of clarity, the defense would like to poll the jury."

As the polling took place, Kathy came to life. Her eyes darted from face to face, as one juror after another repeated the horrible word *guilty*, like the tolling of a bell.

Suddenly, she let out a wrenching, agonizing wail. She threw her body across the table with outstretched arms, pleading with the jurors as they filed out of the courtroom. "No, wait, please . . . don't take my baby from me. Don't give my baby to Peter, please."

The jurors hesitated, their faces reflecting the impact of her words. Ann Polanski, the young schoolteacher, had tears in her eyes. Jon Dalton looked uneasy, awkwardly following her out the door. Eleanor Evans tripped leaving the jury box. The sheriff's deputy lunged to her assistance, but the elderly woman pulled away, straining to hear Kathy cry, "Peter, how could you do this to me?"

As Eleanor Evans got to her room that evening, Kathy's plea continued to rip through her. She wished she could think of something else, but she couldn't.

Something had been gnawing at her, and as she lay between the crisp motel sheets, Kathy's scream still reverberating in her ears, she remembered. She had seen a movie, not more than a week before the trial, about a man who was assaulted and mugged on his way home from work. In the struggle with his assailant, he fell, struck his head on the concrete sidewalk, and died. His wife, some twenty years younger, was accused and convicted of his murder.

The evidence against her was slim: a letter written to a young sailor at sea, professing her love for him. But the jury believed she hired the assailant to murder her husband and sent her to jail.

Proof of her innocence came too late; she'd taken her own life.

*   *   *

The second day of jury deliberations broke clear and cold. The jurors grumbled over their accommodations and the weather, lingering around the coffee machine, reluctant to take their places at the long, narrow table with its clutter of pencils, writing pads, and ashtrays. They had had enough of each other.

Helen, the sheriff's deputy, who had spent the night at the motel with the sequestered jurors, called to them as she unlocked the door to the deliberation room. "It's nine o'clock—time to get back to work."

Dragging their feet, they obeyed. Jon Dalton took a seat at the head of the table next to the foreman, fingering the ashtray before him. He looked around the room, still angry. Ann Polanski took a seat at the opposite end of the table, avoiding his glance. Her smiles and vivaciousness had faded with the onset of the deliberations. One of the two housewives appeared anxious and impatient. She took a seat to Jon's right, snapping, "Let's get this show on the road. I want to get home to my kids."

The foreman stood up and looked down the table at eleven serious faces. "We've got to talk this out this morning," he said firmly. "Sensibly and without emotions."

"We're all talked out!" shouted Jon Dalton. "I say the Kunz woman is guilty all the way to hell! She was ready to kill by pushing the other woman over the cliff; if that didn't work, she was ready to poison her; if that didn't work, she was ready to beat her brains out. What the hell more do you want?" He glowered at Ann from across the table. "She did try all those things, didn't she?"

"No," Ann said, biting her lip. "No, we don't know that. We only know that she thought about doing them. Doesn't it matter how much she's suffered? It's not that cut-and-dry."

For two hours, Eleanor Evans sat in silence, with a yellow pad in front of her. She didn't get mad, she didn't get angry, she didn't argue with anyone. Occasionally, she doodled on the pad, making continuous OOO's across the page.

Suddenly, she stood up. She picked up her chair and carried it to the corner of the room. The other jurors looked at her, puzzled.

"As you know," she explained, "I am retired. I have no clock to punch, no small children waiting for me, and no special place to be. I will not send that poor girl to jail. She has suffered enough. I will sit here until all of you come to your senses." She sat down, her back to the room, and stared at the wall.

The other jurors silently exchanged glances. Discomfited, the foreman started to straighten out the papers before him.

Ann Polanski put her head on the table and began to cry. The sound of a heavy chair being scraped along a wooden floor broke the silence. All eyes shifted toward it. George Lynch, the retired gentleman, impeccably dressed in his gray flannel suit and spit-polished shoes, stood up. His eyes looked bluer than usual.

"If you will excuse me," he said mildly, "I will keep my friend Eleanor company. I, too, am retired, with no special place to be. Sending that young girl to jail will serve no purpose. I believe she has paid her dues." He picked up his chair, placed it next to Eleanor's, patted her lightly on the shoulder, and sat down.

Almost immediately, Ann Polanski bolted from her seat, tears streaming down her face. Kathy's cry had haunted her through the night, and she had regretted having voted at all. She had made one mistake. She would not make another. "I won't let you do this to her. She can't take anymore." She turned a hostile glare on Jon Dalton. "Some things," she said, her voice cracking with resolve, "are not as simple as they look."

*   *   *

Once again, the courtroom was packed. The jurors filed in, one by one, their faces drawn. The foreman handed the deputy a note. Every eye in the room tensely followed it to the judge. Judge Gallucci studied it for a moment. He looked at the defendants for a brief moment, then, spoke to the younger one. "Will the defendant Katherine Kunz please rise?"

Kathy stood up, eyes closed. She looked as if she were going to faint and held on to the table for support. The color drained from her face; she began to shake.

"The jury finds the defendant Katherine Kunz guilty of assault in the third degree."

The courtroom exploded with shouts. The judge banged his gavel as the door burst open and reporters scurried out.

Kathy crumpled in her chair, tears of relief rolling down her cheeks. McCormack had told her that a verdict of assault in the third degree would probably mean probation.

Alice, still angry, jumped out of her chair. "I told ya we din't do nothin' wrong. All they did wuz waste taxpayers' money."

The jurors smiled at Kathy in farewell as they left the jury box. But she didn't notice. She had drifted back to the first time she had ever found herself in a courtroom, the day she and Peter were married. How could things have gone so wrong when she loved him so much? Where was he now?

Suddenly, she heard voices-- excited voices-- and turned to look to the rear of the courtroom. It had almost emptied and the door was swinging like a pendulum. Ann Polanski, one of the jurors, bursting from excitement, ran towards her. She threw her arms around Kathy's neck sobbing, "If you ever go back to Peter again, I'll hit *you* over the head with a frying pan."

Everyone standing around the defense table guffawed with the explosiveness born out of a sudden release of tension.

Kathy did not laugh. Through the embrace of the juror, she looked out the window she had gazed through so often during the trial. She saw Oskar, sitting in the driver's seat of his car, smoking a cigarette, waiting. She closed her eyes and allowed the tears to flow freely down her cheeks. They were not tears of joy, but tears of lost love and wasted years. She knew that her life with Peter was over.

She watched Peter and Penny walk hand in hand to the car, with a beaming Oskar at the wheel, and Kathy knew the dreadful dance would begin anew.

*   *   *

EPILOGUE

Kathy and baby Cara moved to Pennsylvania. In the early '80s, Kathy married a strict, religious widower with six children in an attempt to find some stability. Unfortunately, she continued a tumultuous life. That story will be told in a future book. Kathy died in 2019.

Alice, while visiting Kathy in Pennsylvania, died in her sleep.

Peter and Penny married in 1976 and moved to a rural upstate New York farm, where they had two children. Peter died in 2015 after a long career as a special effects expert in the movie industry.

Hanna, after 30 years of a painful marriage, filed for divorce and fought for custody of King, their German Shepard. After hearing testimony, the Judge awarded Hanna custody of King, proclaiming, "Oskar Kunz isn't fit to raise a dog."

Finally free, the long-suffering Hanna took a vacation cruise to the Bahamas but died tragically in a fiery death aboard the cruise ship.

Oskar regained custody of King and began a new life with an ex-communicated nun he had convinced to leave the order. He was never charged for his sexual crimes as it was very difficult, at that time, to gain a conviction when assault occurred amongst family members.

Gil McCormack practiced law until his death from mesothelioma, which he contracted by working on Navy submarines during WW2. He became a Rockland County judge and was celebrated as Man of the Year by the Rockland County Bar Association just before his death in 1994.

Note: this book is based on true events, actual court proceedings and records, as well as a recounting of events by the people involved. Some names have been changed.

ACKNOWLEDGEMENTS

I would like to thank a number of people, who made this book possible:

First, Helen Bryant, my professor at Rockland Community College, who encouraged me to write this book and edited the original manuscript.

Second, Sue Turnbull, who told me to dust off the twenty-year old manuscript because it was never so topical as right now, during the 'me-too movement.' Sue edited the book and saw it through publication.

Third, my children, Ric and Ron Rooney and Teri Dodaro, who all remember my frenzy of typing while creating the book and always supported my endeavors as a budding author. I'd also like to thank Carlo Rooney and Andrew Turnbull for their design ideas for the book cover.

Fourth, my sister Ann Hickey, my life-long mentor, my surrogate mother and always my biggest cheerleader.

Finally, thank you to Gil McCormack, a wonderful husband, and a fearless defense lawyer, who was dedicated to bringing justice to his clients and to understanding their side of the story.

About the Author:

Tess McCormack was born in Rockland County, New York. At the young age of eighteen, she joined the U.S. Air Force, Communications Department in the Pentagon, Washington, D.C. Married to her high school sweetheart at twenty, she had two sons. Unfortunately, the marriage failed, and Tess found herself in a divorce lawyer's office at the tender age of twenty-eight. That lawyer was Gil McCormack, a war hero who was driven to find justice for the under-dog. The two fell in love, married, and had a daughter. Gil encouraged Tess's love of writing and communication and as a result, she has written two books, numerous published articles and has been a producer, host and writer for both radio and TV shows. As dedicated to helping others as her husband, Tess was honored with an Honorary Doctorate from St. Thomas Aquinas College for her contributions and has served on numerous boards supporting charitable organizations, Rockland hospitals and Hospice funding.